Automatic Detection
of Verbal Deception

Synthesis Lectures on Human Language Technologies

Editor
Graeme Hirst, *University of Toronto*

Synthesis Lectures on Human Language Technologies is edited by Graeme Hirst of the University of Toronto. The series consists of 50- to 150-page monographs on topics relating to natural language processing, computational linguistics, information retrieval, and spoken language understanding. Emphasis is on important new techniques, on new applications, and on topics that combine two or more HLT subfields.

Automatic Detection of Verbal Deception
Eileen Fitzpatrick, Joan Bachenko, and Tommaso Fornaciari
2015

Semantic Similarity from Natural Language and Ontology Analysis
Sébastien Harispe, Sylvie Ranwez, Stefan Janaqi, and Jacky Montmain
2015

Learning to Rank for Information Retrieval and Natural Language Processing, Second Edition
Hang Li
2014

Ontology-Based Interpretation of Natural Language
Philipp Cimiano, Christina Unger, and John McCrae
2014

Automated Grammatical Error Detection for Language Learners, Second Edition
Claudia Leacock, Martin Chodorow, Michael Gamon, and Joel Tetreault
2014

Web Corpus Construction
Roland Schäfer and Felix Bildhauer
2013

Recognizing Textual Entailment: Models and Applications
Ido Dagan, Dan Roth, Mark Sammons, and Fabio Massimo Zanzotto
2013

Automatic Detection of Verbal Deception

Eileen Fitzpatrick, Joan Bachenko, and Tommaso Fornaciari

ISBN: 978-3-031-01030-9   paperback
ISBN: 978-3-031-02158-9   ebook

DOI 10.1007/978-3-031-02158-9

A Publication in the Springer series
SYNTHESIS LECTURES ON HUMAN LANGUAGE TECHNOLOGIES

Lecture #29
Series Editor: Graeme Hirst, *University of Toronto*
Series ISSN
Print 1947-4040   Electronic 1947-4059

Automatic Detection of Verbal Deception

Eileen Fitzpatrick
Montclair State University

Joan Bachenko
Linguistech LLC

Tommaso Fornaciari
Italian National Police

SYNTHESIS LECTURES ON HUMAN LANGUAGE TECHNOLOGIES #29

ABSTRACT

The attempt to spot deception through its correlates in human behavior has a long history. Until recently, these efforts have concentrated on identifying individual "cues" that might occur with deception. However, with the advent of computational means to analyze language and other human behavior, we now have the ability to determine whether there are consistent clusters of differences in behavior that might be associated with a false statement as opposed to a true one. While its focus is on verbal behavior, this book describes a range of behaviors—physiological, gestural as well as verbal—that have been proposed as indicators of deception. An overview of the primary psychological and cognitive theories that have been offered as explanations of deceptive behaviors gives context for the description of specific behaviors. The book also addresses the differences between data collected in a laboratory and "real-world" data with respect to the emotional and cognitive state of the liar. It discusses sources of real-world data and problematic issues in its collection and identifies the primary areas in which applied studies based on real-world data are critical, including police, security, border crossing, customs, and asylum interviews; congressional hearings; financial reporting; legal depositions; human resource evaluation; predatory communications that include Internet scams, identity theft, and fraud; and false product reviews. Having established the background, this book concentrates on computational analyses of deceptive verbal behavior that have enabled the field of deception studies to move from individual cues to overall differences in behavior. The computational work is organized around the features used for classification from n-gram through syntax to predicate-argument and rhetorical structure. The book concludes with a set of open questions that the computational work has generated.

KEYWORDS

credibility assessment, deception detection, factual language, forensic linguistics, gold-standard data, ground truth, high-stakes scenarios, imaginative language, real-world data, stylometry, text classification

Eileen Fitzpatrick: To my husband, Ralph Grishman

Joan Bachenko: In memory of my mother, Claire Joan Baumgartner

Tommaso Fornaciari: In memory of my father, Alberto Fornaciari

Contents

Preface

There are many venues where the ability to spot the lie is an important, often critical, skill. It is necessary in police, security, border crossing, customs, and asylum interviews; in congressional hearings; in financial reporting; in legal depositions; in human resource evaluation; in predatory communications, including Internet scams, identity theft, and fraud; and in false advertising. Discovering lies can thwart serious immediate threats, provide productive directions in the investigation of past events, and assist in the accurate prediction of likely future events.

For much of the 20th century, the fields of psychology and criminal justice have studied the behaviors that might be associated, directly or indirectly, with deception. Three types of behavior have been examined: physiological behavior; vocal behavior, including prosodic features; and verbal behavior, including the words and structures that might correlate with deception.

The study of verbal behavior in deception is relatively new and the attention that natural language processing has paid to discriminating true from false claims is even newer, with most of the work done in the last 10 years as classification techniques have improved. Now is a good time to review the prior literature on deception and consider the NLP approaches that have been tried. Knowing the foundations and trends in work on deception, both theoretical and applied, will enable us to move forward productively.

Several areas of NLP are ripe to address the vocal and verbal features that might be associated with deception and new approaches may well combine information from these with the facial and body movements associated with deception. A spate of recent NLP papers on the classification of narratives as truthful or deceptive suggests that the field is ready to open up to this promising area.

The genesis of this text was a workshop on deception detection that took place as part of the European Meeting of the Association for Computational Linguistics in Avignon in the spring of 2012. The workshop brought together 35 colleagues and offered 14 presentations on work that ranged from annotation tools and corpus building for deception to cross-linguistic classification of deceptive narrative. It also gave the authors of this text an opportunity to work together on our common interest in the use of "real-world" data, primarily legal data, in NLP deception studies.

Following the mission of the Synthesis series, the present text is designed to give the student or researcher in natural language processing a background in the history of deception studies concentrating on the behavioral cues to deception that have been supported in the psychology, applied psychology, and criminal justice literature, a consideration of the real-world data sources for NLP work in deception, a review of NLP work in deception organized around the features used for classification from ngram to rhetorical structure, and a look at exciting questions and areas that need to be addressed in order for the field to progress.

Eileen Fitzpatrick, Joan Bachenko, and Tommaso Fornaciari
July 2015

Acknowledgments

We wish to thank the students who took part in a graduate seminar on current issues in NLP at Montclair State University in which a previous draft of this text was used as the primary text for the course, including Richard Barrett, Janette Martinez, Matthew Mulholland, and Emily Olshefski. Their ability to take the material covered in the text to the next step in their own research gives us confidence that we are respecting the mission of this series.

We would also like to thank Ralph Grishman and Massimo Poesio for input, checking, and fruitful discussions related to the issues in this book.

We are indebted to Myle Ott and another, anonymous, reviewer who provided detailed, thoughtful feedback in their reviews of a draft of the book, and to the series editor Graeme Hirst who first suggested a text on deception in Avignon and has guided it through, with great patience and care, to reality. We are also grateful to the many authors whose work we have cited here.

Eileen Fitzpatrick, Joan Bachenko, and Tommaso Fornaciari
July 2015

CHAPTER 1

Introduction

1.1 INTRODUCTION

Deception occurs frequently in everyday situations, from insincere compliments — "You look great!" — to face saving lies "Can you lend me $5? I lost my ATM card." Most of these lies are inconsequential; some even have positive effects. This book concentrates on the more consequential lies and on the behaviors that are thought to be associated with lying, particularly lying involving natural language. This book discusses how these behaviors are being captured by applications in natural language processing.

The study of deception has deep implications for human, and some animal, behavior since it demonstrates an awareness of self, in particular an awareness that one's own thoughts can differ from those of others [Keenan et al., 2005].

In the broadest sense, deception includes self-deception, acting, and conjuring. It also sometimes covers false statements believed by the teller to be true. This book, however, is devoted to applications where something important is at stake in communication: in police, security, border crossing, customs, and asylum interviews; in congressional hearings; in financial reporting; in legal depositions; in human resource evaluation; in predatory communications, including Internet scams, identity theft, and fraud; and in false advertising. For the purposes of this book, then, we will follow the definition of deception given by Vrij (2008), which excludes self-deception, acting, and falsely held beliefs. Vrij defines deception as a successful or unsuccessful deliberate attempt, without forewarning, to create in another a belief which the communicator considers to be untrue.

The liar can carry out the deception in different ways. The way that immediately comes to mind is the outright lie ("I was not required to approve those transactions"),[1] but liars can be evasive ("Well, there's an issue as to whether I was actually at a—the particular meeting that you're talking about"), exaggerate or minimize an issue ("In that meeting, the power had gone out, and as everybody remembers,...the room was dark, quite frankly, and people were walking in and out of the meeting") or omit significant facts from a story, as did Scott Peterson, convicted for the murder of his pregnant wife, in his detailed account of his actions on the day she was reported missing.

The attempt to spot deception has a long history, dating at least from the Greek physician Erasistratus (300–250 B.C.), who felt the pulse of a suspect to distinguish the lie from the truth

---

[1]The deceptive quotes in this paragraph and the next are from the testimony of Jeffrey Skilling, CEO of Enron, the American energy company, to Congress on February 7, 2002 concerning the accounting fraud that his company had perpetrated.

[Trovillo, 1939], still a measure used in modern polygraphy. While a good deal of research has been devoted to potential physiological cues to deception since the polygraph was invented in 1921, including imaging technologies such as functional magnetic resonance imaging (fMRI) and thermal imaging, visual measures that include body movements, and vocal measures such as pitch and speech rate changes, there is an equally robust literature on the characteristics of language that are thought to be associated with deception. In the psychology and criminal justice literature on deception, these range from discrete cues such as higher rates of negative statements and extreme descriptions ("absolutely, positively no connection") to more global features like lexical diversity and story consistency. To give the scope of work in deception detection, we provide in Chapter 2 an overview of both the non-verbal and verbal studies on deceptive behavior.

The computational literature, which has, to a great extent, replicated the findings of the psychological experimentation, runs the gamut of comparisons of true versus false statements from differences in n-gram occurrences to differences in local features of the narrative to distinctions in rhetorical structure. In its establishment of a baseline against which to measure success, its use of classification algorithms to separate true from false narratives, its training and testing procedures, and its reliance on standard evaluation measures to estimate success, the computational work has the characteristics of much work in applied natural language processing. Unlike many NLP ventures, though, it is hampered by data limitations: it is hard to come by narratives the proposition(s) of which are known to be true or false. We devote Chapter 3 to attempted solutions to this problem.

In addition, computational studies of verbal deception differ from work in other areas of natural language processing in two important, related respects: most NLP studies regard human performance as the gold standard, whereas typical human performance in detecting deception runs at chance levels. This first difference leads to a second: while most evaluations in NLP test against human performance, work in deception detection must test against ground truth, which is external to the verbal data—Was, for example, Enron's Jeffrey Skilling present at that critical meeting or was he not?

1.2   VERBAL CUES TO DECEPTION

Propositional communication takes place through words, and so does the opportunity to misrepresent reality. The most obvious way to detect deception in communication, then, would be to compare the propositions with the reality: if some dissimilarity is found, and the narrator's awareness of that dissimilarity is (reasonably) demonstrated, the communication can be regarded as deceptive.

When doubts about the truthfulness of a communication arise, typically a great deal of effort is directed at establishing the ground truth; getting at this truth is one of the main goals not only in court trials and in police investigations, but also in private disputes. Unfortunately, determining the ground truth in most cases is difficult if not impossible. In such cases, having robust cues to deception would at least lead the inquirer toward communications that are more likely to be lies.

A notable example of the use of linguistic analysis to uncover ground truth dates back to the 15th century, when the Italian rhetorician Lorenzo Valla proved the forgery of the Donation of Constantine, the fake imperial decree which supposedly conferred on the Pope authority over the western Roman Empire. In that case, Valla demonstrated the falsity of the document not only by discussing the historical implausibility of the Donation and addressing a clear mistake with respect to the Donation's date, which referred to a time not compatible with the content of the document, but also by making use of linguistic arguments. In particular, he emphasized that the Latin of the Donation could not belong to the imperial period, but was typical of the following centuries [Valla, 2008].

The study of verbal cues to deception assumes that the style of the communication is affected not only by the demographic, social, and cultural characteristics of the narrator, but also by his state of mind at the moment of the production of the communication. In particular, the basic assumptions of this approach are as follows:

- the psychological condition of the subject affects communication style;

- the elaboration of a lie and the recall of a memory are different cognitive processes; and

- at least in high stakes scenarios, the emotional charge of a lie differs from that of a truthful statement.

It assumes, then, that the communication style of a liar may be different from that of a truth teller. Basically, this is the same idea that characterizes the studies of non-verbal behavior and physiological variables with respect to deception. However, while these studies belong to the research fields of psychology and physiology, the theoretical paradigm here comes from linguistics, and in particular from the structuralist school of thought. The structuralist approach studies texts through the relations existing among their single elements: this mode of reasoning gave rise to the possibility of quantitative and computational analyses of the texts.

The scientific study of deception in language dates at least from Undeutsch, who hypothesized that it is "not the veracity of the reporting person but the truthfulness of the statement that matters and there are certain relatively exact, definable, descriptive criteria that form a key tool for the determination of the truthfulness of statements" [Undeutsch, 1954].

In the last ten years, modern natural language processing techniques have been applied by many researchers to the detection of deception with promising results. This research is covered in Chapter 4. The achievement of these studies is not insignificant, since identifying deception by any means has proven to be a very difficult task, regardless of the kind of cues employed to elicit the deceit. As Aldert Vrij, who has carried out extensive studies of deception within social psychology, notes in referring to the lying protagonist of Italian fable: "a verbal cue uniquely related to deception, akin to Pinocchio's growing nose, does not exist" [Vrij, 2008, p. 103].

Given this situation, the fair success of NLP analyses carried out through machine learning techniques is probably due, at least in part, to the fact that this line of research relies on clusters of cues, which provide an overall picture of the deceptive language. Nevertheless, the effectiveness of machine learning techniques depends equally on the effectiveness of the individual cues, or features, of deception that distinguish the narratives under analysis. Therefore it is worth looking closely at the linguistic features employed in detecting deception in communication.

1.2.1   LINGUISTIC FEATURES USED IN IDENTIFYING DECEPTION

The goal here is to distinguish truthful (T) from false (F) narratives with a high degree of success. To that end, NLP research has borrowed cues to false statements from the psychology and criminal justice literature as well as from standard techniques in natural language processing.

The standard NLP approach uses surface level elements of the narrative—characters, *n*-grams, part-of-speech tags, narrative length, lexical diversity—in a pure classification task. The paucity of data in this field constrains the use of other elements commonly used in NLP, for example, collocational properties.

The data constraints have driven many investigators to generalize over semantically related linguistic elements, for example, self-referencing items (*I, me, my*) as opposed to items that reference others (*you, they, them*). This approach also has the advantage of tapping into psychological motivation for these features; self-references have been found to appear much less frequently in deceptive narratives than in truthful ones, which makes sense if one is trying to distance oneself from the narrative. The most commonly used features here are those of the Linguistic Inquiry and Word Count software [Pennebaker et al., 2007].

In a similar vein, studies have devised objective ways of characterizing certain of the findings from the psychology literature. Verbal and vocal immediacy, for example, are identified by many studies as highly discriminating between T and F narratives as indicated by DePaulo et al. [2003] and have been measured in the NLP literature by presence of active voice, present tense, and self-referencing.

More recently, deeper and/or more global characteristics of the narrative are being investigated to enhance the classification performance. Among these are parse tree differences between T and F narratives. The collection of syntax-related features is more complex than that of surface features, since it requires parsing the narrative in order to identify its syntactic structures, encoded as trees—or parts of trees—of syntactic elements which are used as features of the texts. In the field of deception detection, this approach was followed by Feng et al. [2012a], who found that performance in the classification of narratives as truthful or deceptive was notably better when deep syntactic features were employed instead of shallow syntactic features such as part of speech.

Narrative coherence and discourse relations within the narrative are also under investigation by Rubin and Vashchilko [2012]. This is consistent with work by Susan Adams within the criminal justice field on person-of-interest narratives written prior to police interviews, which notes an imbalance in deceptive narratives among the introduction, body, and conclusion [Adams, 1996,

2002]. Another promising approach creates a profile representative of T narratives against which a test narrative can be measured for compatibility [Feng and Hirst, 2013]. Chapter 4 is devoted to greater coverage of the NLP work on deception.

1.2.2   EFFECTIVENESS OF LINGUISTIC CUES TO DECEPTION

We will see that the variation in the success of T/F classification within NLP depends largely on the contextual factors involved in each study, including the topics, genres, registers, and modes of delivery (face-to-face, written, electronic, etc.). Depending on these factors, classification accuracy rates vary from the low 90% range to the low 60% range, which is still better than the random accuracy of most human judgments.

If we want to achieve classification systems that can generalize across these factors, the field needs to aim for a common data set and shared task against which to test the systems while still identifying the tasks that are more amenable to classification. Several groups are concerned with these issues, including Myle Ott and his colleagues, as well as Fornaciari and Poesio, Rubin and Conroy, and Fitzpatrick and Bachenko. We will consider the issues they raise in Chapters 3 and 5.

As discussed in the previous subsection, a quite wide variety of linguistic variables can be used as deception indicators. Even though none of them can be considered a high probability indicator of deception like Pinocchio's nose, the results of the studies mentioned above suggest that their combination can be useful in identifying deceptive communications.

However, while there have been a large number of studies concerning nonverbal cues to deception, which were even the main focus of a well-known American television series *Lie to Me*, there has been only a relatively small scientific community of linguists, psychologists, and computer scientists dealing with verbal cues to deception. Given that many aspects of speech elude the conscious control of the narrator, such as the aforementioned vocabulary richness, the study of verbal cues to the lie promises to provide valuable support in the difficult task of identifying deception in communication. The state of the art in this field, particularly in its automation, is the object of this text.

1.2.3   VERBAL CUES TO GROUND TRUTH

For studies that use real-world data, the establishment of what is referred to as 'ground truth' usually involves the comparison of a proposition with external data. Jeffrey Skilling, for example, indicated that he may not have even attended a critical meeting until the minutes of the meeting showing Skilling as a participant were produced. However, ground truth can also be verified by attributes of the verbal narrative itself, including the following.

Consistency involves the repetition of the same content in different statements (issued by the same or different subjects).

Contradiction involves two claims the facts of which are at odds with each other.

To make a decision about the truthfulness of a proposition involves the use of the rules of logic, pragmatics, and probability calculus. Even though the modern formalization of these concepts is quite recent, historically the application of these tools to the detection of deception is ancient, and testimonies can be found even in the Bible, for example, in the Book of Daniel (2nd century BCE), where the episode of Susana is described. Here the prophet Daniel unmasks the deceptive accusations of two old judges against the woman (Daniel 13:1-59 Nova Vulgata) by identifying an inconsistency in the different statements that he asked the two judges to issue separately, regarding the same details.

1.3   WHAT'S AHEAD

This book is designed to give someone with an introductory background in natural language processing and/or machine learning an understanding of the current approaches to the automatic detection of verbal deception. This subfield of NLP is in its infancy and so presents an exciting area in which to do groundbreaking work. The purpose of this book is to equip the reader with the information to do that.

Much of the current research in the broader field of deception detection is based on experimental work that attempts to connect specific behaviors with lying. Some work tests connections between physiological measures and lying, while the rest examines behavioral cues tested within the fields of psychology and criminal justice. We begin in Chapter 2 with a brief review of the literature on physiological cues to deception followed by a longer review of the psychology literature based on two overarching works by Bella DePaulo and her colleagues, DePaulo et al. [2003] and Aldert Vrij [2008], as well as work in applied psychology and criminal justice. Chapter 3 deals with sources of deceptive verbal behavior, primarily in the "real world." The heart of the book, Chapter 4, considers issues involved in designing an NLP experiment to test a deception system and examines the current systems that have been built to detect deception, comparing the methods and the results of these systems. Chapter 5 considers open research questions and future directions.

CHAPTER 2

The Background Literature on Behavioral Cues to Deception

2.1 INTRODUCTION

As mentioned in Chapter 1, there is a long history of attempts to link lying to measurable effects on the liar. The effects considered have been physiological in nature—for example, changes in blood pressure or vocal pitch. They have also been cognitive, as are speech disfluencies and repetitions. Emotional effects such as negative affect and verbal uncertainty have also been examined. Both the cognitive and emotional effects can be connected directly to language, as are the examples given here.

The physiological effects are at some remove from language, though vocal changes are more closely connected to it. We include them here to provide a background to the psychology and criminal justice literature, which examines all three types of effects. There are also current attempts to link the verbal effects with the physiological, which we discuss briefly in Section 5.8 of Chapter 5. Finally, the difficulties connecting physiological behaviors to deception demonstrate that the problem of identifying the lie, by any means, is far from solved.

As for the cognitive and emotional effects, there is a rich tradition, dating from Undeutsch, of the study of deceptive behaviors in experimental psychology, where data is obtained by experimentation with subjects in laboratory settings. Another, more recent, thread of studies of behaviors linked to deception comes from the applied psychology and criminal justice literature, where data is collected post hoc from police interviews, court testimony, interviews, and the like. The ramifications of each type of data collection are discussed in Chapter 3; here we examine the literature in the three traditions, reviewing the types of cues, with an emphasis on verbal cues, that have been studied.

2.2 NONVERBAL CUES TO DECEPTION

Nonverbal cues occur independent of language. They include physiological activity, vocalizations, and movements of the face and body. The list in Table 2.1, while not exhaustive, identifies the primary nonverbal cues cited in the lie detection literature and the primary manner of detection for each.[1]

---

[1]See text for references on results greater than chance.

Table 2.1: List of primary nonverbal cues

Cue Type		Cue De-tection	Physical Contact	Results >chance	Commercialized
physiological	respiration, electro-dermal activity, blood pressure	polygraph	yes	yes	yes
	laryngeal frequencies	voice stress analyzer	no	no	yes
	unknown (propri-etary)	layered voice analysis	no	no	yes
	facial blood flow	thermo-graphy	no	yes	no
	electrical brain waves	EEG	yes	yes	yes
	brain blood flow	fMRI	yes	yes	yes
vocal	voice f0, filled pause, silent pause, dis-fluencies, etc.	pitch analyzer, speech editor, manual analysis	no	yes	no
face/body movements	micro-expressions, pupil dila-tion, finger tapping, etc.	video recorder, manual analysis	no	yes	no

Of the cues in this list, physiological indicators are perhaps the most familiar because of their reliance on specialized technologies—polygraph, fMRI, electroencephalography (EEG), etc.—that have allowed the development of systems currently used in threat assessment, criminal investigation, and federal employee screening. Our review begins with this class of nonverbal cues.

Physiological cues and technologies fall into four main categories: polygraphy, voice analysis, facial thermography and brain scans. All assume that lying is a stressful activity that triggers measurable changes in the activity of some physiological system. With the exception of voice stress and layered voice analysis, the proposed physiological cues and related technologies provide at least weak support for this idea.

2.2.1   POLYGRAPHY

Polygraphy is the oldest and best established technology for associating physiological activity with deception-induced stress. Examinees are attached to at least three kinds of physiological data sensors: blood pressure cuff, electrodermal sensor, and respiration sensors positioned on the chest and abdomen [American Polygraph Association, 2010]. The test itself is usually embedded in a longer interview that may last for as long as four hours. At certain points in the interview the polygrapher will ask a series of yes/no questions. Some of these are intended to elicit physiological states that provide baseline measurements, others are intended to elicit departures from the baseline that indicate an emotionally aroused state. Aroused states presumably encode a flight instinct indicative of deception.

Evaluating the polygraph's performance depends on issues that have little to do with polygraph technology. A commonly noted complication is that the physiological states that may indicate deception often arise when deception is absent [National Research Council, 2003, Saxe et al., 1985]. In addition, test outcomes, measured by success in identifying deceptive and truthful subjects, depend largely on the skill of the interviewer, who uses the polygraph as an interrogation tool, and on characteristics of the interviewee, who may be suggestive, anxious, and inexperienced [Saxe et al., 1985]. Finally, polygraphs are well known to be vulnerable to countermeasures, techniques the interviewee can use to deliberately alter physiological states, making it possible for a deceptive interviewee to appear truthful.

Vrij [2008] and the National Research Council Report [2003] raise another concern: standardized methods for representing and scoring polygraph data are difficult to formulate and have yet to be developed. Hence there is no consistent way to tell if failure or success of a polygraph test is due to physiological measurement or to the impressions and experience of the interviewer. Not surprisingly, reports of polygraph accuracy vary widely. The review of polygraph studies by Saxe et al. [1985] cites results of field studies in which correct guilty decisions ranged from 70.6–98.6% and correct innocent decisions ranged from 12.5–94%. The NRC report concludes: "in populations of examinees such as those represented in the polygraph research literature, untrained in countermeasures, specific-incident polygraph tests for event-specific investigations can discriminate lying from truth telling at rates well above chance, though well below perfection" [National Research Council, 2003, p. 214].

Despite these criticisms, the absence of other viable alternatives makes the polygraph a widely used technique for detecting deception. Recent changes in standards of evidence have led several states to admit polygraph results into evidence [American Polygraph Association, 2010].

2.2.2   VOICE ANALYSIS: VSA AND LVA

Voice analysis cues depend on detectable frequencies produced by the body during speech. Two competing methods have been implemented for lie detection: Voice Stress Analysis (VSA) and Layered Voice Analysis (LVA). Both are available as commercial products that are popular with law enforcement professionals.

VSA technology is based on the theory that all muscles in the body, including those of the larynx, vibrate at a rate of 8–12 Hz [Lippold, 1971]. These inaudible microtremors are suppressed when a speaker experiences stress. VSA specialists and vendors claim that their technology is capable of detecting and measuring variations in laryngeal microtremor frequencies. They further claim that these variations are associated with aroused states that indicate deception.

A VSA machine is essentially a computer with VSA software that ostensibly records laryngeal microtremor patterns. The VSA machine may be used in a real-time interview or it may process pre-recorded speech. Several researchers have evaluated VSA devices in laboratory experiments [Haddad et al., 2001, Horvath, 1982] and field tests [Damphousse, 2008]. These studies have failed to confirm that microtremors exist or that VSA technologies can detect them, although there is some agreement with Haddad's [2001, p. 11] conclusion that VSAs are measuring something, but not microtremors. Moreover, despite VSA's popularity in law enforcement organizations, the tests of VSA systems have failed to show that VSA devices perform at a level above chance.

Layered Voice Analysis (LVA) is developed and marketed by Nemesysco. LVA does not use laryngeal microtremors but relies instead on an undocumented signal processing algorithm that employs a "proprietary set of vocal parameters ... new to the world of phonetics" (www.neme sysco.com). The description of LVA technology is too inadequate to support evaluation of its theoretical basis. This leaves performance evaluations, which have failed to provide evidence that LVA performs better than chance in laboratory tests [Harnsberger et al., 2009] and field trials [Horvath et al., 2013]. Despite the poor performance results, law enforcement professionals have reported great success in using LVA and VSA machines to solve crimes [Haddad et al., 2001]. [Horvath et al., 2013, p. 390] speculate that the reported success by field practitioners comes not from the value of the LVA, but rather from operators' ability to "read" the cues inherent in an interviewee's behavior: their tone of voice, assertiveness, directness, naturalness, and so forth. In other words, as with the polygraph, these devices succeed not on their own but only when used as supporting tools in the hands of a skillful and experienced interviewer.

2.2.3   THERMOGRAPHY

Thermal imaging works by using heat detecting cameras to identify warming patterns around a subject's eyes. Warming patterns are formed as a physiological response to stress: blood flow to the area around the eyes is increased, creating increased warmth. Pavlidis et al. [2002] claimed that it is possible to identify a "thermal signature" consisting of blood flow patterns indicative of deception and that these patterns could be used to identify deceptive subjects with "an accuracy comparable to that of polygraph examination." The appeal of this approach is that it offers the possibility of identifying deception without the need for interviews or physical contact. Hence, it would seem to hold great promise for airport and border crossing applications as suggested by Warmelink et al. [2011] and Vrij et al. [2010].

Laboratory studies of thermal imaging show some support for facial thermography patterns as an indicator of deception. In the 2011 airport study by Warmelink, thermal imaging managed to identify liars 69% of the time and truthtellers 64% of the time, a rate that they claim is too low for airport screening, especially given that interviewers working without thermography performed significantly better on the discrimination task. Results of tests by Pollina et al. [2006] suggest a stronger link between facial heat displays and deception. They conclude, however, that the status of thermography remains unclear: "The extent to which thermography will increase accuracy beyond that which is possible using traditional polygraph measures is not yet known" (p. 1189).

2.2.4   BRAIN SCAN: EEG AND MRI

Electroencephalography (EEG) and functional magnetic resonance imaging (fMRI) are well-established technologies for the measurement of brain activity. Their relevance to deception analysis lies in the demonstrated ability of EEG and fMRI measurements to distinguish the brain's responses to known information from responses to novel information. Hence, these technologies could be used to determine, for example, whether a suspect has special knowledge of a crime that only a guilty person would have. There exists an extensive research literature on memory and EEG/fMRI as well as significant commercial development in the United States (www.brainwavescience.com) and India (www.axxonet.com).

EEGs record brain waves called event related potentials (ERPs). The ERP memory recognition response is the P300, so named because the response usually occurs 300–900 ms after information relating to the memory is presented. The P300 response fails to occur if the information is unfamiliar and hence may be viewed as a diagnostic to determine if a subject has experiential knowledge of some event.

The measurement of P300 responses forms the heart of commercialized EEG/P300 systems that claim to detect memories indicating a suspect's guilt. Two of the strongest challenges to EEG/P300 systems come from studies of false memories and countermeasures. Allen and Mertens [2009] found that subjects' ERP responses failed to show a distinction between true recollections and false recollections that were implanted by association with true memories, opening up the possibility of deeming an innocent person guilty. In a study of countermeasures, Bergström et al. [2013] were able to demonstrate that, contrary to previous claims, ERP activity can be deliberately suppressed. EEG/P300 technology, like the polygraph, is thus vulnerable to countermeasures that guilty suspects may employ in order to appear innocent.

fMRIs measure blood flow changes in the brain. They have been shown to find activity in regions of the brain that laboratory tests associate with actual memories. The twelve laboratory studies reviewed by Vrij [2008] all found that "areas associated with inhibition and conflict resolution were activated when lying" (p. 368). However, Vrij goes on to observe that, for each study, "a somewhat different brain activity pattern emerged as an indicator of deceit" (p. 369), suggesting that a uniform fMRI-detectable cue was nonexistent in the reported data. Fabricated memories create additional challenges. In their experiment on memory detection and faces, Rissman et al. [2010] found that brain activity recorded by fMRI failed to show differences between true and false facial memories.

Despite the doubts about fMRI cues to deception and the lack of field evidence, fMRI for lie detection has been commercialized with claims of accurate lie detection ranging from 90–99% (www.noliemri.com).

2.2.5 VOCAL CUES

This class of indicators comprises speech sounds that lack semantic content. These sounds include filled pauses, silent pauses, disfluencies, and variations in rate and pitch. Studies of vocal cues often report a weak correlation with truthful vs. deceptive conditions but they also tend to yield conflicting results [DePaulo et al., 2003, Vrij, 2008]. Evidence for a relationhip between rising pitch and deception, however, is consistent across reports. For example, in their widely cited nurses' study, Ekman and Friesen found a significant increase in pitch when the subjects reported feeling stressed [Ekman and Friesen, 1974]. Streeter et al. [1977] also documents an increase in pitch and amplitude for laboratory subjects in a deception task. Graciarena et al. [2006] combined vocal cues, including acoustic cues not usually examined in deception experiments, with mixed results. Tests with prosodic features only—pitch, duration and energy—and tests with spectral features only yielded accuracies of 62.7% and 60%, respectively, in both cases a gain over chance. Elkins et al. [2012] offer one of the few field studies of vocal cue effectiveness. Pitch variations and eye gaze were recorded as part of a border crossing venue in Europe. Although details are left vague, Elkins et al. found a significant correlation between departures from the F0 baseline and deception; no effect was noted for eye gaze.

Vrij [2008, p. 62] argues that deception researchers have failed to provide a set of "consistent and reliable nonverbal cues," in part because the research community lacks sufficiently detailed methods for identifying and measuring vocal and other nonverbal cues. Standardization of data descriptions and experimental protocols are needed to ensure progress in this area. For example, distinguishing different classes of filled pause (*uh* vs. *um*), disfluency (word repetition, word fragment, false start and repair) and silent pause (duration and position in sentence) would undoubtedly help to clarify the contribution of each data type in any experimental paradigm.

2.2.6   BODY AND FACIAL MOVEMENTS

In their review of nonverbal deception cues, DePaulo et al. found pupil dilation to be the most strongly supported, with the vocal cues of pitch and disfluency close behind [DePaulo et al., 2003]. Ekman [2001] and Ekman and Friesen [1974] showed that barely detectable facial expressions—microexpresisons—encode information about emotional states that may indicate deception. These microexpressions happen quickly and are nearly impossible for people to control, making them a likely source of valid information about emotional state. Yet, as with polygraph and other emotion detectors, evidence of particular emotions may have many sources other than deception.

Data collection for nonverbal cues is a difficult task. For example, microexpressions, which are fleeting and subtle, must be studied with a frame by frame analysis of video—a laborious and expensive project. Unlike fMRI and other approaches to deception studies, there is no existing technology that can perform the analysis of facial cues although there are efforts to automate facial coding (e.g., Chu et al. [2013]) that may have profound effects on this area of deception research. A similar observation might be made for the application of automatic speech recognition (ASR) technology to research on vocal and linguistic cues.

2.3   THE PSYCHOLOGY LITERATURE

Within the psychology literature, wide coverage of the behavioral correlates of deception has been given by an extensive meta-analysis of the literature done by DePaulo et al. [2003]. Aldert Vrij [2008] provided another comprehensive review of the field. The following section offers an overview of this work. Both DePaulo et al. and Vrij, couched within the framework of social psychology, have served as reference points for most of the subsequent computational work in deception; they not only contribute to our knowledge of deception but can also function as resources for creative new approaches to its detection. For this reason, we include some discussion of the non-verbal cues considered in these works while concentrating on the aspects that pertain to verbal behavior.

2.3.1   DEPAULO ET AL.'S STUDY

DePaulo et al. [2003] defines deception as a "deliberate attempt to mislead others," excluding cases where the subject misinforms in good faith. More interestingly, they only take into consideration the cues which "can be discerned by human perceivers without the aid of any special equipment" [DePaulo et al., 2003, p. 74]. Such a choice implies that the authors focus on cues of deception which can be recognized in real time.

The final data set for the meta-analysis includes 120 independent samples from 116 studies, and reports 1,338 estimates of the discriminatory effectiveness of the 158 cues to deception considered. In doing so, it covers the main theoretical approaches to deception detection of the 20th century (the literature review ended in 2002). The authors also formulate and test their own hypotheses, relying on the vast amount of results available through their review.

In the next section we introduce the approaches to deception detection considered by De-Paulo et al. [2003], including their own theoretical framework, followed by a presentation of the methods employed in the research, the main results of the literature on cues of deception, and the outcomes of analyses carried out.

The main approaches to deception detection
DePaulo et al. [2003] discuss three approaches to deception detection that are consonant with the approach of DePaulo et al. and their methodological premises:

- the work of Ekman [Ekman, 2001, Ekman and Friesen, 1969, Ekman et al., 1985, 1991];

- the work of Zuckerman [Zuckerman et al., 1981, 1982, Zuckerman and Driver, 1985]; and

- the work of Buller [Buller and Burgoon, 1996, Buller et al., 1996].

Here we discuss the work of each group.

THE STUDIES OF EKMAN
Ekman's research relies on the idea that strong emotions can activate facial muscles auto-matically, and that the resulting "micro-expressions" could be cues to deception [Ekman, 2001]. More precisely, he distinguishes two different kind of signals that subjects may display.

Leakage cues are behavioral expressions that the liar fails to squelch and that are strong and lasting enough to reveal what they unsuccessfully try to conceal: the truth.

Deception cues share the same nature as leakage cues, suggesting deception but without reveal-ing the truth.

For example, if a subject tries to deny anger, he will have to suppress typical signs of anger, such as narrowing of the lips, lowering of the eyebrows, and so on. But this task is difficult, since emotions can arise suddenly. According to Ekman [2001], subjects can suppress their expressions within 1/25 of a second, but this lapse of time is enough, for a trained observer to detect such expressions. Similarly, several authors [Ekman et al., 1985, Ekman and O'Sullivan, 2006, Hess and Kleck, 1990, Hill and Craig, 2002] found that spontaneous and deliberate expressions are different in latency time, overall duration, duration of peak intensity, and onset and offset time (the time from the start of the expression to its peak and from the peak to its disappearance, respectively).

In order to analyze those expressions, Ekman et al. [1985] and Ekman [2001] distinguish between different emotions associated with deception that could differentiate liars from truth tellers. In particular, they consider cues of the following.

Fear. This emotion is believed to depend on the stakes involved in the telling of the lie and may be expressed by higher pitch of voice, faster and louder speech, pauses, and errors [DePaulo et al., 2003].

Guilt. Even though it seems difficult to determine cues to guilt, "they could include cues to sadness such as lower pitch, softer and slower speech, and downward gazing" [DePaulo et al., 2003].

Delight. Lastly, even positive emotions may be associated with the act of telling lies, such as excitement due to the challenge of the task and euphoria or pride when the lie is accepted as true, called by Ekman [2001] "duping delight."

However, Ekman is aware of the ambiguous nature of the signs of emotion, and points out that it is a mistake "to presume that concealed emotion is evidence that a person is lying about the topic of interest to the interviewer" [Ekman, 2003]. This is what Ekman calls the "Othello error," in reference to the Shakespearean character's misreading of his wife's display of emotion [Ekman, 2001]. In fact, Ekman warns that "emotions do not tell you their cause" and cues of fear are the same, whether the speaker is afraid of being caught in a lie or disbelieved when telling the truth [Ekman, 2003].

THE FOUR FACTORS OF ZUCKERMAN ET AL.

Zuckerman et al. [1981] also assume that behaviors specifically related to deception cannot be found; therefore they try to identify a pattern of behavioral expressions, non-specific in themselves—or, more precisely, deriving from general cognitive and emotional processes—that have a greater probability of appearing when subjects lie rather than when they are telling the truth. In particular, they hypothesize that cues to deception might be found by exploring the following factors:

Emotional reactions. Zuckerman et al. assume that feelings of guilt and fear of being unmasked may be associated with the act of lying. Therefore, liars could exhibit signs of anxiety as well as verbal and non-verbal behaviors indicating an unconscious attempt to put a distance between themselves and their deceptive communications. The authors call such distancing "nonimmediacy" and suppose that liars might seem evasive and indirect.

Cognitive effort. Liars have to accomplish several cognitively demanding tasks. First, they have to formulate narratives different from the truth they know. They also have to monitor the plausibility of their statements and avoid contradictions in their stories. Last, but not least, they have to check the reactions of their interlocutors, tuning their behavior accordingly. As a consequence, Zuckerman et al. expect liars to show more hesitations, more speech latencies and fewer gestures of illustration than truth tellers.

Attempted behavioral control. In order to be convincing, liars have to monitor not only the content they are conveying, but also their verbal and non-verbal behavior. This task could be difficult, since some bodily reactions, such as the tone of voice [Ekman, 1981], are normally beyond voluntary control [Ekman, 2001]. The authors therefore argue that in deceptive communication discrepancies between verbal and non-verbal expressions, or between different non-verbal behaviors, should occur to a larger extent than in a truthful one.

Arousal. Even though typical signs of general arousal, such as higher pitch, pupil dilation or frequent blinking might be found during deceptive communication, Zuckerman et al. admit that they can be explained by the factors cited above. In fact, arousal and emotional reactions display as the same collection of physical phenomena, and so are not distinguished in research activities, as noted by Vrij [2008].

THE INTERPERSONAL DECEPTION THEORY OF BULLER AND BURGOON

While the studies of Ekman and of Zuckerman et al. focus especially on the liars, and consequently on the cues to deception they may disclose, Buller and Burgoon [1996] and Buller et al. [1996] put special emphasis on the interaction between subjects, as the determinant factor for the expression of signs that may reveal deception. Buller and Burgoon claim that the difficulties in lying mentioned above might be not constant during the communication; rather they tend to dissolve, as the liar, more and more, takes control of the interaction based on the feedback he receives. The feedback, in turn, depends on the expectations, motivations, and aims of the liar as well as the liar's relationship to the target. Given this premise, Buller and Burgoon formulate their Interpersonal Deception Theory focusing on the motivational dynamics of the communication, and in particular identifying three kinds of goals in deceptive communication:

Instrumental, that is, related to the practical results the lies are aimed to obtain, such as "establishing, maximizing, and maintaining power or influence over the receiver, acquiring and protecting resources" [Buller and Burgoon, 1996, p. 216];

Relational, which refers to the effect the liar pursues in regulating the relation with the interlocutor, for example "avoiding interpersonal tension or conflict, maintaining and redirecting social interaction" [Buller and Burgoon, 1996, p. 216];

Identity goals, which concern the liar's efforts with respect to "avoiding shame or embarrassment, projecting a more favorable image, enhancing or protecting self esteem" [Buller and Burgoon, 1996, p. 216].

The motivation to deceive leads the liar to carry out **strategic behaviors**, aimed at managing the content and style of the communication to maintain the credibility of the message. The point is that when the management of the behavior is "carried to extremes, it may result in an overcontrolled or rigid presentation, inexpressiveness, and reduced spontaneity, which qualify as **nonstrategic behaviors**" [Buller and Burgoon, 1996, p. 217]. In other words, the insight of Buller and Burgoon consists in the fact that "strategic intentions may produce nonstrategic byproducts in the form of noninvolvement and performance decrements" [Buller and Burgoon, 1996, p. 218].

In particular, Buller and Burgoon claim to have found evidence that the deceiver's effort to manipulate the communication affects both its content and the concurrent behavior: "Deceivers have been found to manage information in the form of verbal content that is incomplete, nonveridical, indirect, vague, uncertain, hesitant, brief, and disassociated from the sender; to manage behavior through a submissive and formal demeanor and reduced nonverbal immediacy; and to manage image through increased pleasantness and relaxation over time. They have simultaneously also leaked nervousness, arousal, and negative affect (at least initially) and suffered performance impairments such as nonfluencies and poor impressions" [Buller and Burgoon, 1996, p. 218].

The Self-Presentational Perspective of DePaulo et al.

The Self-Presentational Perspective of DePaulo et al. derives from the attempt of the authors to synthesize the best intuitions of the previous approaches, while trying also to overcome their weaknesses. The first point they underline is that lying is a common practice in daily life; studies where subjects note their lies show that they tell an average of one or two lies every day.

Due to their high frequency, DePaulo et al. believe that not all lies really require many cognitive resources or imply strong emotional involvement: "Lies based on scripts or familiar stories are unlikely to be marked by the signs of mental effort" [DePaulo et al., 2003, p. 79]. It is assumed that people do not plan nor do they feel much guilt about such lies. Nevertheless, DePaulo's analysis rests on the assumption that these lies can be distinguished from truthful statements: "cues to deception ordinarily are quite weak. There are, however, conditions under which cues are more apparent." [DePaulo et al., 2003, p. 77]. DePaulo et al. seek to explain the cues as coming from "people's attempts to control the impressions that are formed of them"—what DePaulo et al. refer to as "self-presentation"—because of the "prevalence of self-presentational themes in the kinds of lies that people most often tell."

DePaulo et al. see liars as less capable of embracing their lies, which may result in narratives with fewer details than truthful ones. They also view liars as feeling a greater sense of deliberateness than truth tellers and the impression of low involvement of the liar in the interaction. They may fail in evaluating the feedback of the receivers, and this affects the effectiveness of the attempted self-regulations. Lastly, from an emotional point of view, and consonant with the literature in this field, DePaulo et al. expect that deceivers may experience more negative emotions than truth-tellers. These emotions can vary from shame and guilt to fear of being unmasked. Consequently, deceivers may seem "less forthcoming, less convincing, less pleasant, and more tense" [DePaulo et al., 2003, p. 78].

One of the novelties of the theoretical perspective of DePaulo et al. is that they stress the idea that even honest actors usually try to manage the impression they give to interlocutors. Nonetheless, they predict that some behavioral expressions may be associated with deceiving communication. DePaulo et al. claim their approach "has the advantage that the behaviors of interest are clearly defined and objectively measured" [DePaulo et al., 2003, p. 82].

From the point of view of the so-called "hard sciences," these "advantages" are rather minimal requirements for any research activity; the fact that the authors present them as such is a clear symptom of the difficulties the researcher has to face in studying deception. In fact, the possibility of precisely measuring the variables is a central issue in scientific research; however, DePaulo et al. do not exclude the possibility that social actors, who rely just on subjective impressions, may be able to detect deception as well as, and possibly better than, objective measurements. For this reason, they also include subjective measurement in their systematic review of the literature. We discuss the methods and results of this review in the next sections.

Methods of literature analysis

The studies in the DePaulo et al. review include only those in which the behaviors associated with deceptive communications were compared with those associated with truthful communications and only those in which the cues studied were both objectively and subjectively measured. They thus exclude research on physiological variables that are not directly detectable by human observers. The analysis was also limited to studies involving adult, English-speaking subjects. Studies in which subjects had to participate in role-playing were also discarded: the authors consider only experimental designs where the participants had to express genuine truths or lies.

CUE IDENTIFICATION

Following these criteria, DePaulo et al. considered 120 independent experimental subject samples from 116 published studies. From these studies, they identified 158 different behaviors that were considered possible cues of deception. They were, in turn, divided into five macro-categories, designed to test the hypotheses stemming from the self-presentation theory [DePaulo et al., 2003, p. 83], according to which the liars were predicted to be the following.

Less forthcoming. The cues used to test this assumption concern the length of the narrative, its complexity and the amount of information provided by it.

Less compelling. The cues here test the plausibility of the narrative and the speaker's certainty and degree of involvement in it. Cues involving speaker immediacy, fluency and animation were also inserted into this category.

Less pleasant. These cues test for the degree of positive feelings and emotions.

More tense. This group involves the behavioral signs typically associated with tension and anxiety.

Less spontaneous. According to the last category of DePaulo et al., lies should appear less affected by the imperfections that normally characterize truthful narratives. These include spontaneous corrections, superfluous details, contextual embedding and, in general, a mixed bag of narrative imperfections.

As mentioned above, the objective measurement of the cues is critical to the evaluation of the relation between cues and deception. Unfortunately, this is not an easy task. In fact, the cues were considered **objectively** measured when their size was precisely known, and **subjectively** measured when the evaluation relied simply on the subjective impressions of the observers. The evaluation of the effect of the cues follows from this distinction. In the first case, in fact, the effect was **precisely calculated** as well; in the second it was possible to determine only the **direction** of the effect. Lastly, some cues were indicated in the reports as not significant; in such cases, not even the direction of the effect was knowable.

CUE EVALUATION

DePaulo et al. define the effect size d for each cue as "the mean for the deceptive condition (i.e., the lies) minus the mean for the truthful condition (i.e., the truths), divided by the mean of the standard deviations for the truths and the lies [Cohen, 1988]" [DePaulo et al., 2003, p. 89]. Therefore, when d is positive, the behavior appears more frequently in association with lies than with truth; and the other way around when d is negative. In some reports, mean and standard deviation were not provided, but other statistical parameters were available: in such cases, DePaulo et al. employed other relevant methods for evaluating the effect size. When the effect of a cue was indicated as not significant and no more information was given, the authors set $d = 0$; if the direction of the effect was known but not the size, they conservatively set $d = +0.01$ or $d = -0.01$. As a result of the analysis, DePaulo et al. found 1338 effect sizes, of which "787 could be estimated precisely, 396 were set to zero, and 155 were assigned the values of ± 0.01" [DePaulo et al., 2003, p. 89-90]. There were 27 cues showing an effect size greater than ± 1.50.

In order to obtain the estimate of the effect size of each cue, the mean was calculated over all occurrences of the cue per speaker and over all occurrences of the cue within the sample. Each independent sample was counted as a single measure of the cue regardless of the size of the sample. Studies that involved a greater number of subjects, that is to say the studies which provided the most reliable results, were more heavily weighted.

Lastly, in order to ascertain if the effect sizes were significant across independent samples, DePaulo et al. employed the homogeneity statistic Q [Hedges and Olkin, 1985], whose p thresholds depend on the likelihood that the variance in effect sizes was due to sampling errors.

CUE MODERATORS

DePaulo et al. predicted that certain factors will moderate the effect size of the cues. These include the following.

Motivation to lie

Identity-relevant incentives where the task concerned the subjects' professional skills or some other valued competence, such as their intelligence.

Instrumental incentives in which the subjects received some kind of economic or material reward.

Both. Lastly, the authors classified separately the studies where both inducements were provided to the subjects.

Opportunity to plan the narrative

> **Planned** in which subjects were given preparation time, removing some of the mental effort involved in lying. Liars could show longer responses with shorter response latencies.

> **Unplanned** in which subjects were required to respond spontaneously. DePaulo et al. hypothesize that here lies are more likely to be shorter, less consistent, and show disfluencies and other signs of mental effort.

Duration of messages

> Longer messages may impose "greater cognitive burdens" on the liar, making cues to deception "clearer and more numerous."

EXPERIMENTAL DESIGNS

The studies were considered **within subject** if the same actors had to give true and false statements; **between subjects** if truthful and untruthful narratives were issued by different subjects. The studies, in turn, were divided according to the paradigm of their experimental designs and recoded into two categories: lies involving transgressions, where DePaulo et al. hypothesized that the cues would be clearer, and those not about transgressions. The experimental paradigms were categorized as follows; we include the number of studies involving each paradigm.

Transgressions

> **Mock crime** (8 studies) in which subjects have to "steal" some money, and then lie about the mock theft.

> **Cheating** (8) in which subjects were required to cheat and then lie about it.

> **Naturalistic** (4) in which subjects lied "of their own accord" in real-life circumstances with their statements later determined to be lies.

Non-Transgressions

> **Beliefs** (44) involved scenarios where subjects were expected to lie or tell the truth about personal beliefs or opinions.

> **Image description** (16) in which subjects were asked to view images and lie or tell the truth about what they were seeing.

> **Guilty knowledge/Card test** (8) in which subjects lie about something they know or what card they have selected from a deck.

> **Person description** (7) in which subjects give truthful and false descriptions of their feelings regarding people they know.

> **Job interview** (6) in which typically the subject has to convince an interviewer of qualifications they do not actually possess.

Personality scale (3) in which subjects lie or tell the truth about responses they have given on a personality scale.

Pain experience (3) in which the deception concerned some pain really felt but dissimulated or, by contrast, simulated but not really felt.

The degree of interaction in the experimental conditions was also assessed by the authors, who distinguished four situations.

Full interaction in which the participants interacted freely and expressed themselves without any constraint determined by the experimental design.

Partial interaction involved some kind of structure that was imposed on the communication, typically a set of pre-ordered questions.

Non-direct interaction in which the participants were in the same environment but did not interact with each other. In this case there is no direct communication, and the reciprocal influence of the actors is limited to that of being present in the same environment.

Absence of interaction in which the subjects were left completely alone when carrying out the experimental task.

Lastly, DePaulo et al. categorized the cues as being assessed objectively or subjectively in each study since their self-presentation model predicts that subjective impressions would be more powerful discriminators of true vs. false. Indeed, around 20% of estimations of the cues of deception came from subjective impressions of untrained raters [DePaulo et al., 2003]

AGREEMENT

The coding of the study characteristics was implemented by three annotators, who were trained before the task and who each coded two-thirds of the studies. The discrepancies between coders were then discussed and resolved in conference. The whole corpus of studies was also coded by Bella M. DePaulo, who discussed the remaining discrepancies with a fourth coder.

Unfortunately, DePaulo et al. did not provide any measure of the agreement between coders, which would have been useful in evaluating the reliability of their classification. However, they claim that the agreement was nearly perfect for the evaluation of the least ambiguous variables, as well as for the dimension "transgression vs. non-transgression" [DePaulo et al., 2003, p. 89].

Report Statistics

DePaulo et al. provide statistics for the reports they analyzed. In 52 of the 120 independent samples considered, the subjects received some incentive to lie. An interesting detail concerns the duration of the truthful/deceptive messages: only 36 studies reported duration, and in 28 of them the duration was $\leq 1\ min$. The fact that several cues of deception were produced in such a short span of time leaves open the question of how they might evolve over time in a long narrative.

Lastly, with respect to the inter-rater agreement on the cues, "Of the 1338 estimates of the 158 cues to deception, 273 (20%) were based on the subjective impressions of untrained raters" [DePaulo et al., 2003, p. 90]. The fact that the rate of estimates which do not rely on objective measures does not exceed 20% is good. The reliability of rater judgments and the agreement between human coders, in fact, is a thorny issue in scientific research. With respect to this, it is worth quoting Massimo Poesio on his work with anaphora resolution: "Subjects do not even agree on whether a pronoun is there or not." No need to say that the presence or absence of a pronoun should be unambiguous; even so, rater opinions can be quite inconsistent. *A fortiori*, this problem can be expected when it is a matter of evaluating much more shaded items. Therefore, the fact that most estimates were objectively measured is a remarkable point which supports the reliability of the results.

Results

In presenting the results, DePaulo et al. follow the scheme shown in Section 2.3.1, discussing each of the hypotheses that follows from their self-presentation perspective on deception. The same approach is adopted here. Unless otherwise noted, we report here only the significant results. DePaulo et al. report as positive differences $(+d)$ behaviors associated with lying and as negative differences those associated with truth-telling.

Hypothesis 1: liars are less forthcoming than truth-tellers

The authors evaluated the length of the response as the first index of the approachability of the subjects. They claim that this is the feature of the messages most often reported in the literature; nonetheless they found only a "tiny and nonsignificant effect in the predicted direction $(d = -0.03)$" [DePaulo et al., 2003, p. 91]: deceptive messages would be shorter than truthful ones. Clearer outcomes, however, were found regarding the duration of talk time and of the interaction: liars talked less than truth-tellers $(d = -0.35)$; and interactions were shorter when a liar was present $(d = -0.20)$.

Liars also supplied fewer details than truth-tellers $(d = -0.30)$, a finding which is consonant with the hypotheses of the authors. Following the assumpions of the reality monitoring theory, discussed in Section 2.4 they also expected that deceptive messages would contain less sensory-related information, but they found only "a nonsignificant trend in that direction $(d = -0.17)$" [DePaulo et al., 2003, p. 91].

With respect to non-verbal behavior, the only cue that was significant concerned the tendency of liars to press the lips together more than truth-tellers $(d = +0.16)$: in this case too the predictions of the authors, who expected less friendly behaviors from liars, were supported.

Hypothesis 2: liars are less compelling than truth-tellers

The experimental results supported the second hypothesis of the authors as well. In fact, liars' narratives were judged to be significantly "less plausible $(d = -0.23)$; less likely to be structured in a logical, sensible way $(d = -0.25)$; and more likely to be internally discrepant or to convey ambivalence $(d = 0.34)$" [DePaulo et al., 2003, p. 92]. Liars were also significantly "less involved verbally and vocally in their self-presentations" ($d = -0.21$) and, as far as non-verbal behavior is concerned, they exhibited fewer illustrative gestures during the narrative ($d = -0.14$).

In order to estimate the immediacy of the communication, the authors made use of a set of cues that had been the object of study of other authors [Fleming, 1994, Mehrabian, 1977] and which they collapsed into three composite measures.

Verbal immediacy. DePaulo et al. are cautious in the use of this category, citing precise objective measures of immediacy such as those described by Wiener and Mehrabian [1968], including "the use of the passive rather than the active voice, the use of negations rather than assertions, and looking away rather than maintaining eye contact" [DePaulo et al., 2003, p. 81-82], but noting that other cues have been cited in the literature and skilled observers of social behavior "can discriminate truths from lies by their subjective impressions of the constructs of interest (e.g., distancing) just as well, if not better, than can objective coding systems." DePaulo et al.'s analysis shows that liars appear generally less immediate than truth-tellers by a significant margin ($d = -0.31$). In particular, they seemed to employ more linguistic expressions which were judged to put a distance between themselves and the interlocutors as well as the content of their statements. They also seemed to be "more evasive, unclear, and impersonal" [DePaulo et al., 2003, p. 93].

Non-verbal immediacy was measured through the impressions of the observers and the relation between cues and deception was non-significant, although the trend was in the expected direction ($d = -0.31$).

Verbal and vocal immediacy. As in the previous case, these cues rely on subjective judgments. However, in association with the verbal immediacy composite measure, they showed a significant effect ($d = -0.55$).

Even though the aggregation of cues to immediacy gave appreciable results, the effect of most of the individual cues was inconsistent. For example, it is noteworthy that eye contact and gaze aversion were not significant cues of deception. This is in contrast with what is commonly believed about deceptive behavior. A possible explanation of this result may rely on the fact that social actors are highly aware of their management of eye contact and are able to control it, exercising countermeasures. The expression of this kind of behavior may also be regulated in a more complex way, as discussed in the section on Moderators below.

A further relevant parameter that affects the extent to which a speaker appears compelling is the sense of uncertainty which accompanies the narrative. According to the subjective evaluations, liars seemed to be more uncertain than truth-tellers ($d = +0.30$).

However, this impression does not carry over to the category of speech disfluencies. With respect to this, DePaulo et al. embrace the distinction proposed by Kasl and Mahl [1965] between the so-called **"ah" disturbances**, which usually fill the pauses when the content to be expressed is particularly complex, and the **"non-ah" disturbances**, which consist in interruptions and changes in the sentences, stutters, omission of words, and slips of tongue, which are considered a sign of anxiety. The most frequently reported cues of this kind, combined with silent pauses, were not significant, while the repetition of words and phrases was a significant cue to deception ($d = +0.21$). Such an outcome suggests that the complexity of the task of lying implies an absorption of cognitive resources, which has the peculiar effect of making the language more stereotyped, which might be a productive distinction with respect to linguistic analysis.

As far as the non-verbal behavior is concerned, the authors found that liars tend to raise the chin significantly more often than truth-tellers ($d = +0.25$). This is actually a quite surprising result, as raising the chin is usually considered a sign of dominance in the social interaction and of certainty, while the liars seemed to be more uncertain than sincere actors. By contrast, other non-verbal behaviors which may convey some sense of uncertainty, such as posture shifts, hand movements, and foot or leg movements, did not show any clear relationship with deception. Therefore these outcomes seem to suggest that the non-immediacy, the uncertainty, and, in general, the lesser involvement which characterize the verbal expressions of the liars tend not to be correlated with analogous behaviors on the level of body language.

HYPOTHESIS 3: LIARS ARE LESS POSITIVE AND PLEASANT THAN TRUTH-TELLERS

This hypothesis also received some confirmation from DePaulo et al. Liars turned out to issue more negative statements and complaints than truth-tellers ($d = +0.21$), and they also were perceived as less pleasant ($d = -0.12$), and significantly less cooperative ($d = -0.66$).

As in the previous case, less clear results come from the non-verbal behavior. For example, "the 27 estimates of smiling produced a combined effect size of exactly zero" [DePaulo et al., 2003, p. 96]. However, the authors address the fact that, in the studies of smiling, only two distinguished estimates of genuine smiles and two feigned smiles. Such reports concerned the simulation of emotions, and not surprisingly it turned out that, when the subjects were pretending to feel positive emotions, genuine smiles were produced less often ($d = -0.70$) and, by contrast, feigned smiles were more frequent ($d = +0.31$).

HYPOTHESIS 4: LIARS ARE MORE TENSE THAN TRUTH-TELLERS

Even though not all cues of deception were significant, most of their values were in the direction expected by the authors. Moreover, as far as significant results are concerned, liars were found "more nervous and tense overall than truth tellers ($d = +0.27$)" and "more vocally tense ($d = +0.26$)" [DePaulo et al., 2003, p. 96]. They also showed higher pitch of the voice ($d = +0.21$) and more dilated pupils ($d = +0.39$). Cues of fidgeting, when comprehensively considered, were significant as well ($d = +0.16$). However, the studies that distinguished between different types of fidgeting gave non-significant and inconsistent results with respect to the direction of the effects: ($d = +0.08$) for facial fidgeting, ($d = -0.12$) for object fidgeting, and ($d = -0.01$) for self-fidgeting, suggesting that fidgeting cues are not reliable predictors of deception.

HYPOTHESIS 5: LIARS ARE MORE STEREOTYPED THAN TRUTH-TELLERS

DePaulo et al. predict that deceptive narratives present "fewer ordinary imperfections and unusual contents" than truthful ones [DePaulo et al., 2003, p. 96]. Indeed, the authors found that spontaneous corrections are less frequent in deceptive stories ($d = -0.29$). The tendency of liars to give fewer details was non-significant, but the trend was in the expected direction ($d = -0.16$). By contrast, liars showed a greater tendency to mention facts of secondary importance with respect to the central point of discussion ($d = +0.35$).

Also consonant with their prediction, the authors found that liars admitted lack of memory less frequently than truth-tellers ($d = -0.42$). This is an interesting outcome, which deserves more consideration.

Cue Clustering

All researchers who deal with deception detection, following whatever approach, conclude that a single cue specific to deception cannot be identified. However, DePaulo's study shows that particular *sets* of cues, unspecific in themselves, may be indicative of deception. To determine the "right" set of cues, however, is not a trivial task, because many cues turned out to give inconsistent indications across different studies; this difficulty is further complicated by the fact that constellations of cues may be peculiar to a given speaker. A possibility that should be taken into consideration is that deceptive behaviors, whether verbal or non-verbal, may be strongly affected by the context in which they are generated. The liars' admissions of lack of memory may constitute a clear example of this idea. While DePaulo et al. found that liars are reluctant to admit lack of memory, a recent study concerning deception in a particular context clearly showed the opposite trend [Fornaciari and Poesio, 2013]. In this study, statements issued during debates in Courts were analyzed. During these hearings the subjects were often accused of having committed acts in violation of the law by the prosecutor. In this situation, a fairly typical strategy on the part of the subjects, pointed out by the judges themselves, was to lie by denying any memory of the acts, probably because this seems a socially allowed way of removing themselves from their responsibilities. This suggests that in different contexts different cues of deception may be disclosed. DePaulo et al. seem to accept this idea. In fact, they conclude their study by considering the interaction between some variables—some related to context conditions—and the observation of cues to deception. The effect of such variables, which the authors call "moderators," is discussed in the next section.

Moderators

In order to evaluate the interaction between the cues to deception and the cue moderators, discussed above, DePaulo et al. considered only cues for which at least 10 precise estimates were available, as they needed a sufficient number of estimates for each level of the moderator variables. There were 18 cues to deception that met this criterion, 4 of which produced no significant effects, leaving 14 cues to consider with respect to the moderating influences of motivation to lie, opportunity to plan, and duration of message.

MOTIVATION TO SUCCEED AT LYING

According to their predictions, DePaulo et al. found an interesting effect of the motivation to succeed at lying on the expression of deception cues. For example, eye contact, which was not significantly different in liars and truth-tellers when no particular incentives were given to the subjects, was significantly reduced in liars who were in some way motivated to succeed ($d = -0.15$). The same was true for foot or leg movements ($d = -0.13$). In the other direction, motivated lying produced significantly more nervousness and tenseness ($d = 0.35$) and significantly higher-pitched voices ($d = 0.59$).

In the presence of some particular motivation, also *non-ah* disturbances and filled pauses showed interesting changes: they were non-significantly more frequent in the absence of incentives, but the trend inverted in the presence of some inducement: the cues became significantly less frequent in liars ($d = -0.10$ and $d = -0.13$, respectively).

IDENTITY-RELEVANT MOTIVATIONS TO SUCCEED

DePaulo et al. had supposed that liars would give shorter answers than truth-tellers and would have shown longer response latency and more silent pauses: these predictions were not confirmed in the general analyses. However, when identity-relevant motivations were taken into consideration, the cues "response length" and "response latency" showed "nearly significant effect sizes" [DePaulo et al., 2003, p. 97] in the expected direction ($d = -0.23$ and $d = +0.38$, respectively).

As in the general analyses, liars produced significantly higher voice pitch than truth-tellers ($d = +0.67$), and significantly fewer foot or leg movements ($d = -0.28$) in the identity-relevant condition, although non-significant in the overall analyses.

INSTRUMENTAL MOTIVATIONS

In the studies where instrumental—that is economic—incentives were given to the subjects, "there were no effect sizes that differed significantly from chance" [DePaulo et al., 2003, p. 97]. However, *non-ah* disturbances and filled pauses showed the same trend inversion which was seen in the general "motivation to succeed" condition, with almost significant d values, ($d = -0.17$ and $d = -0.14$). The fact that instrumental motivations did not strongly affect the expression of cues to deception is consonant with the self-presentational perspective of DePaulo et al., which predicted a stronger effect in the case of identity-relevant motivations.

UNPLANNED AND PLANNED PRESENTATIONS

Seven reports analyzed by DePaulo et al. explored the difference between planned and unplanned responses. Due to the small number of studies and the fact that only two cues—response length and response latency—could be based on at least three independent estimates, with two precisely estimated, the authors warn that the remaining results should be considered with caution [DePaulo et al., 2003, p. 98]. In order to evaluate the effect of the variable, the authors subtracted the effect size of planned messages from that of unplanned messages. The difference in response latency was significant ($d = +0.20$); in particular, when the messages were unplanned liars tended to show longer latencies, while when the message was planned liars' latencies were relatively shorter than those of truth-tellers. In unplanned presentations, the length of liars responses was shorter, as expected, but not significantly so as was the case also for silent pauses, which occurred more frequently in liars' presentations, although not as a significant differentiator.

DURATION OF THE PRESENTATIONS

DePaulo et al. also considered the mean duration of the presentation of liars. Since duration is a continuous variable, the subjects were not divided into groups; instead, the authors employed the mentioned Q_B statistic, which measured the homogeneity of the effect sizes, where beta indicated the direction of the effect. The results showed that "when presentations were sustained for greater amounts of time, deceptive responses were especially shorter than truthful ones ($b = -0.008$), and they were preceded by a longer latency ($b = +0.034$)" [DePaulo et al., 2003, p. 100]. Subjects, especially in the longest presentations, also spoke in a higher pitch when lying ($b = +0.002$).

COMMUNICATIONS THAT WERE OR WERE NOT ABOUT TRANSGRESSIONS

As predicted by DePaulo et al., whether a narrative is about a transgression is a variable that had a considerable effect on deception cues. When transgressions were the topic, relative to when they were not, liars spoke significantly faster ($d = +0.32$ vs. $d = +0.01$), blinked more ($d = +0.38$ vs. $d = +0.01$), moved feet and legs less ($d = -0.24$ vs. $d = -0.04$), and were found more tense ($d = +0.51$ vs. $d = +0.09$); none of these cues was significant in the non-transgression condition. In the transgression condition, some other non-significant trends were also found, which suggest that liars tended to reduce *non-ah* disturbances ($d = -0.24$ vs. $d = +0.17$), eye contacts ($d = -0.13$ vs. $d = +0.04$) and lastly undifferentiated fidgeting which was, by contrast, significant from the point view of the non-transgression condition ($d = -0.16$ vs. $d = +0.24$).

INTERACTIVITY

The degree of interaction was also found to be a relevant factor that enhanced the expression of some deception cues. Liars in interactive conditions gave fewer details ($d = -0.33$ vs. $d = -0.06$), spoke in a higher pitch ($d = +0.35$ vs. $d = -0.06$), and blinked ($d = +0.29$ vs. $d = -0.06$) more than truth-tellers, while in non-interactive paradigms the difference in these cues was not appreciable.

CUES MEASURED OBJECTIVELY AND SUBJECTIVELY

Lastly, the authors considered the effect sizes of the cues with respect to whether the study involved objective or subjective evaluation, as they had hypothesized that human observers might have been more effective than objective measurements. They analyzed six cues here: amount of detail, vocal/verbal immediacy, nonverbal immediacy, eye contact, facial pleasantness, and relaxed posture. They found that the difference between the two conditions was significant in three cases (details, vocal/verbal immediacy, and facial pleasantness), and in all cases the effect size was stronger when subjectively evaluated. This outcome would suggest that human observations of some behavioral cues may be more accurate than an objective measure.

While we do not exclude this possibility, nonetheless our opinion is that human evaluation should be handled very carefully, as the agreement between human judges and sometimes even the definition of the cues, is often a not negligible issue in scientific research.

Conclusion

DePaulo et al. carried out a wide analysis of the literature, which reveals how difficult it is to evaluate the possible cues to deception, as the relation between deception and the single cues is usually weak. Indeed, in the conclusion of their study they state that "behavioral cues that are discernible by human perceivers are associated with deceit only probabilistically. To establish definitively that someone is lying, further evidence is needed" [DePaulo et al., 2003, p. 106].

Nonetheless, thanks to the size of their data collection and to the rigor of their methodological approach, the study of DePaulo et al. represents a fundamental stage in the modern research on deception, stimulating the researcher to follow new paths. Aldert Vrij smartly expressed this idea: "A turning point in our thinking about lie detection came in 2003. In that year, Bella De-Paulo and her colleagues published a meta-analysis of deception research that demonstrated that nonverbal and verbal cues to deception are typically faint and unreliable. It made us realize that a new direction in deception research was required" [Vrij and Granhag, 2012, p. 4]. The new direction is the object of the next section.

2.3.2   VRIJ'S STUDIES

Aware that, as wide scientific evidence shows, deception cues are usually weak and often unreliable, Aldert Vrij supports research activities not aimed at finding out new and more reliable cues—which is an approach he considers doomed to fail—but at manipulating the interactions with subjects in order to enhance the expression of the deception cues already known.

Basically, Vrij considers two methods of producing an increase in the number and variety of deception cues leaked by experimental subjects:

Imposing emotional load. This is the path followed, for example, in the techniques of police interrogation developed by Inbau et al. [2011], where non-cooperative subjects are put under some form of psychological pressure in order to elicit emotional reactions which may be considered, in turn, cues to deception. The problem with such techniques is that, as we try to emphasize above, emotional reactions are not specific to deception. The same kind of issue concerns methods that rely on the evaluation of physiological variables, where the correlation with deception is also not unequivocal. As a consequence, physiological reactions and emotional responses might be considered cues to deception when they are, in fact, related to other internal psychological states. In other words, such techniques are prone to false positive errors, which, in cases like police interrogations, could lead to serious consequences. The doubts, not to say the certainties, regarding the degree of accuracy of such strategies in detecting real deception cues, along with the ethical concerns that arise from the use of stressful techniques, has induced researchers to adopt a different perspective in recent studies.

Imposing cognitive load. In contrast with the stress-inducing approach, the techniques proposed by Vrij rely on the idea that increasing the difficulty of the cognitive tasks given to the subjects does not remarkably affect the behavior of the truth-tellers, while it does enhance the leakage of cues to deception from liars. This claim is based on the notion that "if lying requires more cognitive resources than truth telling, liars will have fewer cognitive resources left over" [Vrij and Granhag, 2012].

There are many ways in which cognitive load can be increased. In particular, Vrij and Granhag [2012] suggest two main strategies, from which they derive several tactics that are briefly discussed in the next subsections.

The approach of Vrij can be summarized as follows:

1. to increase the difficulty of recalling information, ask subjects:
   - to tell their stories in reverse order
   - to maintain eye contact with the interviewer
2. to induce the subjects to be more talkative:
   - inform subjects that truth-tellers are more talkative than liars
   - instruct the interviewer to be particularly supportive
   - pose unanticipated questions

Discussing these methods, Vrij and Granhag [2012] draw an explicit comparison with "accusatory interview approaches," highlighting the fact that in those cases interviewees have to face accusations, while "the cognitive load approach solely uses information-gathering questions" [Vrij and Granhag, 2012, p. 114]. Furthermore, the authors point out that "accusatory questions lead to short denials (e.g., "I am not lying," "I did not do it") that do not require fabricating much detail" [Vrij and Granhag, 2012, p. 115]. By contrast, information-gathering questions have two advantages: they "are more cognitively demanding for liars" and in themselves they do not tend to evoke emotional reactions. Therefore, the authors claim that not only do "information-gathering interviews result in more verbal cues to deceit," but also that "nonverbal differences between truth-tellers and liars, which are subtle by nature, are therefore most likely to occur in response to information-gathering questions." [Vrij and Granhag, 2012, p. 115] Last, but not least, a meta-analysis on the topic [Meissner et al., 2012] showed that, while information-gathering methods decrease the likelihood of false confessions, accusatory interviews increase the likelihood of both true and false confessions.

The next subsections discuss experiments that employ cognitive-load methods.

Increasing the difficulty of the recollection

RECALLING THE EVENT IN REVERSE ORDER

Vrij et al. [2008] carried out an experiment where truth-tellers and liars were asked to recall an event in chronological and reverse order. They applied the typical "mock theft" paradigm: while the truth-tellers had to honestly recall an event where they had not committed a mock theft, the liars had to deny their responsibility for the mock theft they had committed. Both truth-tellers and liars were told they would be rewarded if they were successful in convincing the interviewer of their innocence, while the interviewer was blind with respect to the condition of the interviewee. However, in both groups, half the subjects were asked to tell the event in chronological order, and half had to recall it in reverse order.

The results confirmed the expectations of the authors: "participants in the control condition showed only one cue of deceit: liars moved their hands and fingers less than truth tellers" [Vrij et al., 2008, p. 259]. By contrast, "In the Reverse Order condition liars included fewer auditory details and contextual embedding details and more cognitive operations in their stories than truth tellers, three signs of cognitive load. Furthermore, liars made more speech hesitations, spoke with a slower speech rate, and made more speech errors than truth tellers, which are three more signs of cognitive load. Liars, however, did not just reveal more signs of cognitive load than truth tellers. They also made more leg and foot movements than truth tellers and blinked more. These are signs of nervousness, rather than signs of cognitive load" [Vrij et al., 2008, p. 259].

The purpose of the researchers, however, was not simply to verify the relation between cognitive load and deception cues; they were also interested in estimating the extent to which these cues to deception could be exploited by observers not specifically trained for the task. They carried out a second experiment, where police officers had to give a judgment regarding the truthfulness of subjects in the first experiment, both in control and in reverse order conditions. While in the first condition the performance of the police judges did not exceed the chance level, in the second it did, as the liars were found to be more nervous and displayed a need to think harder than truth-tellers. This second result is remarkable, as it suggests that the cognitive load approach can be particularly useful in real-life scenarios.

MAINTAINING EYE CONTACT WITH THE INTERVIEWER

Another study by Vrij et al. [2010] follows the same scheme as the previous one, with the difference that, in this case, the subjects were instructed to maintain eye contact with the interviewer while recalling the event. In this case also, the experimental design consisted of the mock theft paradigm, where truth-tellers and liars had to recall the event with and without constant eye contact with the interviewer. As with the reverse order situation, the hypothesis was that maintaining eye contact is cognitively demanding, thereby inducing more cues to deception.

Even though the direction of the outcome matched the authors' expectations, the results were weaker than in the previous study. In fact, in the eye contact condition, both liars and truth tellers mentioned fewer auditory and temporal details, spoke slower, and increased eye blinks and hand/finger movements. These are, as the researchers themselves underlined, signs of nervousness rather than cognitive load, indicating that the eye contact condition may affect both cognitive processing and emotional reactions. Nonetheless, in the eye contact condition, two variables significantly differentiated truth-tellers from liars: "Liars included fewer spatial details into their account than truth tellers and told their story in a more chronological order" [Vrij et al., 2010].

In spite of these not particularly impressive results, the eye contact condition helped untrained student observers to detect deception. The second experiment of this study, in fact, showed that only in this condition could they distinguish between lies and truths, even though in this case too the effect was not particularly strong. In conclusion, the authors admit that the cognitive load imposed by the eye contact condition may have been overrated, hypothesizing, for example, that the difficulty of the task could be reduced by practice. Even so, Vrij et al. [2010] remark that the observers' performance in lie detection benefited by this technique, and conclude that required eye contact could be employed as a tool for deception detection.

Inducing subjects to speak more

In another recent study, Vrij and his group jointly investigate the effect of interviewer demeanour and unexpected questions [Shaw et al., 2013]. In particular, the study, trying to reproduce the police interrogation scenario, which is often conducted by more than one officer, employed two interviewers, one of whom posed the questions, while the second, who remained silent, was presented as an expert in deception detection. On this basis, a $2 \times 2 \times 2$ experimental design was created, where the behavior of liars and truth tellers was evaluated with respect to the demeanour adopted by each of the two interviewers, which could be either neutral or supportive. Supportive behavior consisted in "leaning forward, nodding and smiling when the participants answered," while when they adopted a neutral demeanour "the interviewers kept an open posture but largely did not respond to the participant's answers. They were also conscious, however, of not appearing negative or disbelieving" [Shaw et al., 2013, p. 339].

In addition, the subjects were asked to answer expected and unexpected questions; in particular, they were required to recall an event involving the preparation of a room for a seminar in both chronological and reverse order. In order to evaluate the statements of the subjects, four dependent variables were examined: the frequency of visual and spatial details in the normal and reverse order recollections, the frequency of normal order temporal connectives in normal order recollections, and the frequency of reverse order temporal connectives in reverse order recollections. As with the experiments described above, truth-tellers had to carry out and later to describe some activities, while the liars committed a mock theft and had to pretend to have done the same things as the truth-tellers.

The most remarkable result of the study was the effect related to the silent interviewer who, when supportive, significantly elicited an increased leakage of cues to deception, specifically with respect to the amount of detail in responses, with "liars providing more detail in the expected question and fewer details in the unexpected question" [Shaw et al., 2013, p. 341]. This outcome confirmed the authors' hypotheses that liars can prepare for expected questions and, particularly in the presence of a supportive silent interviewer, are motivated to provide many details, but they are unable to prepare for unexpected questions.

It may seem surprising that the effect of the silent interviewer was stronger than that of the questioning interviewer, in particular because subject gaze toward the silent interviewer was lower than 10% of the overall interview time. The researchers propose two explanations for this phenomenon. First, the subjects were explicitly told that the silent interviewer was particularly expert in deception detection, and even the limited amount of gaze is sufficient to detect his/her demeanour. Moreover, the speaking interviewer gave two kinds of signals, speech and demeanour, and the first could have interfered with the second, while the silent interviewer only communicated through his/her demeanour.

Lastly, the authors examined the use of temporal connectives in the reverse order condition. They found that "Liars used the connective 'before that' less often than truth tellers, whereas there was no difference for the 'and then' connective. The truth-tellers' experience of the event they recalled during the interview was inherently different from liars' experience. As a result, truth tellers may have had a more coherent reverse order script of their activities, reflected in the increased use of reverse order temporal connectives" [Shaw et al., 2013, p. 342].

Conclusion

The core idea of the recent studies of Vrij and his research group is that the deception detection problem can be addressed using methods aimed to enhance the expression of deception cues, rather than to find new cues which, especially if singularly considered, would probably turn out to be weak and unreliable. The use of special techniques, however, is not completely new. The prescription of recalling an event in reverse chronological order, for example, belongs to the cognitive interview [Fisher and Geiselman, 1992], a well-known tool for optimizing the collection of information in police investigation from cooperative subjects. The novelty consists in the purpose of the application of this techique, which is used not only to enhance the amount of information provided by the subjects, but also to strengthen possible cues to deception. This approach is very reasonable and, we think, destined to affect best practices in testimony collection, especially in the case of uncooperative subjects. Obviously, the methods Vrij is developing could also be useful from the perspective of linguistic analyses, which can benefit from an increased expression of linguistic cues to deception, as the additional language encouraged by the design of the experiments shows.

2.4   THE FORENSIC LITERATURE

The fields of applied psychology and criminal justice, which draw their data from criminal cases and/or provide support for the use of specific techniques and tools for forensic applications, are also a source of insight into deceptive behavior. These fields have spawned several approaches to verbal deception that we cover here. The approaches capitalize on differences between experienced events and imagined events. Recent work on the relationship between deceptive opinions and imaginative writing in the CL community makes this area of forensics particularly relevant here.

2.4.1   STATEMENT ANALYSIS

As described in Vrij [2008], Statement Analysis had its origins in a question posed by the West German Supreme Court in 1954 as to whether psychologists could assess the credibility of child witnesses in sexual abuse cases—a type of real world case that often lacks independent verification. The result was a requirement that psychological assessments be done in all such cases, with "a comprehensive list of criteria" first provided by Undeutsch [1967]. The criteria, all considered attributes of truthful, i.e., experienced, accounts of an incident, included anchoring of the account, concreteness, wealth of detail, originality, internal consistency, and mention of details specific to the type of case. Undeutsch also identified manifestations of these criteria, including reference to details exceeding the child's capability to understand, reporting of subjective experiences, mentioning of unexpected complications, spontaneous corrections, and self-deprecating interspersions.

Susan Adams, a psychologist and FBI investigator, adapted Statement Analysis to the written narratives of adult suspects and victims of criminal incidents [Adams, 1996, 2002, Adams and Jarvis, 2006]. Adams looked at 60 narratives, for which investigative evidence had determined 30 narratives to be true and 30 deceptive. The narratives had a mean word count of 497 words and a range from 26 words to 6,089. Adams tested six attributes, or cues, for their correlation with either truthful or deceptive narratives, and found that there was a strong positive relation between deception and three cues—equivocation, negation, and relative length of the narrative prologue. One cue, unique sensory details, showed a strong positive relation with truth, while verbal expression of emotion was weakly associated with truth. Quoted discourse, which previous work by Raskin and Esplin [1991], Steller and Köhnken [1989], and Undeutsch [1989] had found to be associated with veracity in oral narratives, showed no such relation in Adams' narratives.

Using the six cues, Adams tested various regression models on their ability to discriminate the true from the deceptive narratives. She found that the model that represented the frequency of each cue divided by the total word count—Adams' density ratio model—for the entire narrative as well as the word count percentages of the prologue partition was the best predictor of the veracity of each narrative, classifying 82.1% of the narratives correctly overall, with 79% of the truthful narratives and 85% of the deceptive narratives correctly classified.

Most of Adams' cues, chosen because of their relevance to written narrative, were taken from the psychology literature, including both work covered in DePaulo et al. [2003] and work from Statement Analysis. However, the idea that narratives have a beginning, a middle, and an end, with deceptive narratives having a longer beginning (possibly to cover for the unknowns in the skimpy middle) comes from the forensic work of [Rabon, 1996, Rudacille, 1994] and [Sapir, 1987].

2.4.2   STATEMENT VALIDITY ANALYSIS

Statement Analysis has evolved into a systematic credibility assessment instrument known as Statement Validity Analysis (SVA), which has roots in both Germany and Sweden [Trankell, 1963]. SVA provides a set of tools to assess veracity in child witnesses in sexual abuse cases, although it has been extended to adult witnesses in other areas. The SVA approach concentrates on attributes of truthfulness and asks the basic question "What is the source of this statement?

Does the statement describe personal experiences of the witness or does it have another source?" [Köhnken, 2004].

There are four stages to an SVA analysis: (1) a background case-file analysis in which hypotheses about the source of the statement are generated, (2) a semi-structured interview, (3) an analysis of the content of the interview, and (4) an evaluation of stage (3) based on a validity checklist.

Stage (3) is referred to as criteria-based content analysis (CBCA), which is performed by highly trained analysts on transcripts of the interview. It consists of 19 criteria judged on a three-point scale: "0" if the criterion is absent, "1" if the criterion is present, "2" if the criterion is strongly present. It is "based on the hypothesis that statements based on memory of one's own experiences differ in certain content features from fabricated statements" [Köhnken, 2004]. All the criteria are associated with truthfulness; lying can only be inferred from a low score. The criteria, from Steller and Köhnken [1989], with explanations added in parentheses, are the following.

- General characteristics

    1. Logical structure (statement is coherent and logically consistent);

    2. Unstructured production (information is presented in non-chronological order);

    3. Quantity of details (statement is rich in details).

- Specific contents

    4. Contextual embedding (events are placed in time and location);

    5. Descriptions of interactions (statement has information that links the alleged perpetrator and witness);

    6. Reproduction of conversation (specific dialogue, not summaries of what people said);

    7. Reporting of unexpected complications during the incident.

- Peculiarities of content

    8. Unusual details (tattoos, stutters, individual quirks);

    9. Superfluous details (details that are non-essential to the allegation);

    10. Accurately reported details misunderstood (mentioning of details outside a person's scope of understanding);

    11. Related external associations;

    12. Accounts of subjective mental state (description of a change in a subject's feelings during the incident);

    13. Attribution of perpetrator's mental state (witness describes perpetrator's feelings).

- Motivation related contents

    14. Spontaneous corrections;

    15. Admitting lack of memory;

    16. Raising doubts about one's own testimony;

    17. Self-deprecation;

    18. Pardoning the perpetrator.

- Offence-specific elements

    19. Details characteristic of the offence.

The subjective nature of many of the CBCA criteria raises the question of inter-rater relia-bility. Vrij's 2005 SVA review found that "Many inter-rater agreement rates were above .75, and interestingly, all three studies in which inter-rater agreement was calculated for the total CBCA score fell in this excellent range. . . . These findings suggest that total CBCA scores are more reliable than scores for the individual criteria" [Vrij, 2005].

2.4.3   REALITY MONITORING

In 1981, Marcia Johnson and Carol Raye proposed a cognitive model that sought to differentiate the operations of the mind that distinguish a remembered external experience from a remembered internal thought. Additionally, they were interested in how and why these two different types of memory may sometimes be confused. The model proposed "Dimensions on which the classes of externally generated and internally generated memories typically differ." The model posits that external memories have more contextual attributes (e.g., more spatial and temporal information), more sensory attributes, and more semantic detail (i.e., "more information or more specific in-formation,") while internal memories include more information about cognitive operations (i.e., self-generated information like "She must have been running") [Johnson and Raye, 1981]. The processes by which one decides whether a memory has an external or internal source they dubbed Reality Monitoring (RM). To provide an empirical basis for the model, Johnson developed a 39-item Memory Characteristic Questionnaire (MCQ) [Johnson et al., 1988].

Researchers in deception found RM particularly appealing because, while Statement Va-lidity Analysis provides a set of heuristic tools, RM's cognitive model provided "a theoretical basis concerning why truthful statements should differ from invented accounts" [Sporer, 1997].

From a factor analysis of the MCQ, Sporer provided eight "subscales," including:

1. clarity;

2. sensory experiences;

3. spatial information;

4. time information;

5. emotions and feelings;

6. reconstructability of the story (despite complexity of the action; presumed and factual consequences and certainty/doubts about the memory);

7. realism; and

8. cognitive operations.

The items of the scale "serve as the basis for any further analyses," with subscales (1)–(7) expected to occur more in truthful statements, and cognitive operations more in deceptive statements.

As with CBCA, the subjective nature of the RM coding has prompted inter-rater reliability assessments. Sporer [2004] reports agreement scores from [Strömwall et al., 2004] "above $r = .71$, except for Realism, for which it was only $r = .52$."

As far as the performance of RM tests is concerned, Vrij [2008] compares the reported accuracy of 10 studies that tested both CBCA and RM. The total accuracy score across the 10 studies for CBCA was 63.63, for RM 68.80, and for the two combined 74.00, high enough to suggest an empirical basis for verbal differences between accounts of experienced events and imagined ones.

Conclusion

Statement (Validity) Assessment and Reality Monitoring are based on what is referred to by Steller as the Undeutsch Hypothesis, which holds that "statements which are based on memories of real (self-experienced) events are different in quality from statements which are not based on experience but are mere products of fantasy" [Steller, 1989]. These approaches provide attributes, sometimes of a somewhat subjective nature, of verbal narratives that may be worth considering in attempts to distinguish truthful from deceptive accounts automatically. Reality Monitoring also provides an explanation of why these accounts might be different. The explanation is well worth considering in light of recent work by Ott et al. [2011] that finds a relationship between deceptive opinion spam and imaginative writing, a topic we address in Chapter 5.

2.5 FORENSIC IMPLEMENTATIONS OF THE LITERATURE

A number of language-based methods have been proposed for assessing the likelihood of truth and deception in written and spoken statements by suspects, victims, and witnesses. These are implementations that draw upon empirical observations of forensic practitioners as well as the methods originally formulated for CBCA. They are not intended to provide or even favor a theoretical framework beyond the essential Undeutsch hypothesis. According to Adams [1996], all versions make two critical assumptions: (i) language can provide information about the veracity of a narrative independent of factual content and (ii) it is possible to describe procedures for analyzing linguistic cues so that people who are taught the procedures can become more proficient at discriminating truth from deception. Several techniques have been developed primarily for use by law enforcement and related practitioners. The best known is Scientific Content Analysis (SCAN) developed and marketed by the Laboratory for Scientific Interrogation (LSI, www.lsiscan.com).

2.5.1   SCAN AS AN INVESTIGATIVE TOOL AND TRAINING PROGRAM

SCAN and other statement analysis systems are used and taught by practitioners throughout the world according to Vrij [2008]. Their popularity speaks to a strong need for systems of veracity assessment that are both reliable and practical. Yet few researchers have attempted to conduct the studies that would validate or disprove the claims of SCAN and other statement analysis methods. Porter and Yuille [1996] are among the first to emphasize the need for empirical evidence that can justify the reliance on linguistic cues in forensic applications: "Empirical studies had been conducted only on the utility of some of these clues with witnesses or victims (or analogs of these populations) or uninvolved undergraduates. As for crime suspects, the evidence originates only from anecdotes or the unmerited assumption that the findings with witnesses/victims were generalizable to this population. Given that many police forces are being trained in how to identify deceptive statements based on certain verbal clues, it is important that the validity of these clues be established or negated" [Porter and Yuille, 1996, p. 444].

A handful of studies have examined SCAN with suggestive but inconsistent results. Two studies, Driscoll [1994] and Smith [2001], are aimed at evaluating SCAN as a field method for veracity assessment and as a training method, respectively. Adams and Jarvis [2006] examine the performance of a subset of SCAN criteria on their forensic data. Porter and Yuille [1996] and Nahari et al. [2012] examine SCAN's performance on laboratory data in contrast with the theoretically grounded approaches of Reality Monitoring and CBCA. With the exception of Porter and Yuille, whose data source is spoken interviews, the SCAN studies rely on written statements describing the incident under investigation. This is in keeping with SCAN's preference for written statements prepared without the influence of a questioner.[2] The studies have little in common other than their focus on SCAN criteria and provide only moderate support for SCAN's claims at best. However, the case for or against SCAN is far from closed.

2.5.2   EVALUATIONS OF SCAN

Driscoll [1994] has two goals: (i) to evaluate LSI's claim that SCAN can discriminate between statements that are likely true and those that are likely false; and (ii) to propose a quantitative evaluation measure that is similar to the scoring system used in CBCA and that would provide more informative and consistent results than the qualitative evaluation typically used in SCAN assessments. The study examines ten SCAN criteria, listed in Driscoll's Appendix, that are emphasized in SCAN training workshops. The data set consists of written statements that were voluntarily

---

[2]Other systems, e.g., Rabon [1996] and Clark [2008], are intended for use in spoken interviews as well as written statements.

Table 2.2: Outcome of SCAN assessment adapted from Driscoll [1994, p. 84]

	Positive Scores	Negative Scores	Total
likely truthful (AAS)	8	3	11
likely false (DS)	1	18	19

obtained from 30 suspects just before taking a polygraph test. The statements were scored using a 5-point scale (-2, -1, 0, $+1$, $+2$) to indicate the presence or absence of a SCAN criterion. Positive values indicated truthfulness, negative values indicated deception, and zero indicated that a criterion was not present in the statement. Driscoll explains: "For example, if the subject made changes in the language in the statement, a -1 could be assigned as the score for that criterion. But if no changes in the language were observed in a particular statement, the assigned score would be a $+1$ or $+2$, depending on the length of the statement." [Driscoll, 1994, p. 83]. The scoring results showed a significant difference between likely true (AAS) and likely false (DS) statements as Table 2.2 shows.

Although these results provide some support for Driscoll's approach, only one criterion stands out when the results are broken down by indicator type: denial of allegations and lack of denial are the strongest indicators of truthfulness and deception, respectively. As Driscoll observes, these results should only be considered suggestive. The statements represent a small sample limited to the files of a single polygrapher and SCAN assessments were performed by a single rater. It also appears from a concluding comment that the ground truth assessments were known by the rater assigning SCAN criteria assessments: "Future research will need to include a blind analysis of the statements, where the evaluator has no knowledge concerning the cases" [Driscoll, 1994, p. 85].

Adams and Jarvis [2006] test six criteria cited in statement analysis applications and research. A subset of these are used in SCAN: equivocation, emotions, and narrative balance. In the literature and SCAN documentation (LSI SCAN workshop, 2004) equivocation is usually referred to as uncertainty or hedging, e.g., *I think, kind of, to the best of my knowledge*. The emotions criterion refers to the number and location of emotion words. When these words occur in the beginning of a narrative, they indicate a fabricated account; the presence of emotion words in the description of the incident and its epilogue is consistent with truthfulness. Narrative balance is an important element of SCAN analysis. It refers to the structuring of the narrative into three parts—prologue, incident, and epilogue—where truthfulness is indicated when the incident description makes up around half of the narrative. According to SCAN, a lengthy prologue can often be associated with deception.

Adams and Jarvis found a strong relation between statement structure and deception—narratives in which the prologue is lengthy by comparison with the incident and epilogue sections is more likely to be a fabrication. They also identified a positive relation between equivocation and deception. With respect to emotions, the results showed "a mild positive relationship between veracity and density of emotions in the epilogue partitions of the examined statements. No relationships were found between veracity and emotions in the remaining sections [Adams and Jarvis, 2006, p. 16]. These results would seem to provide empirical support for SCAN's claims about the significance of narrative balance, equivocation, and the location of emotions. However, some questions remain as to exactly how the researchers managed the assignment of ground truth and the assessment of deception/veracity categories and whether these tasks were performed by different people [Adams and Jarvis, 2006, p. 12].

Finally, as a visit to the LSI website will show, SCAN's primary activity is the marketing of SCAN training. Workshops on SCAN's approach and methods are conducted by SCAN experts—often law enforcement professionals—and offered in a series of progressively more complex training sessions. The initial workshop is a two- to three-day course focusing on the SCAN criteria and their application to written criminal statements. Smith [2001] conducted an evaluation of SCAN training in order to determine whether SCAN should be used in educating British police detectives. Subjects for the study were police officers that fell into three general categories— (i) officers with some knowledge of SCAN; (ii) experienced detectives with no knowledge of SCAN; and (iii) newly recruited officers with no exposure to SCAN. Smith's [2001] study showed that group (i) (officers with exposure to SCAN) and group (ii) (experienced detectives who relied on intuition) both performed significantly better in identifying deception than the novice officers who had no SCAN training and relied on intuition (group iii). While providing modest support for LSIs claim that SCAN improves detectives ability to assess veracity, these results were viewed by Smith [2001] as insufficient to justify the investment in a national training program.

Laboratory Tests of SCAN Criteria

Two laboratory studies, Porter and Yuille [1996] and Nahari et al. [2012], examine the effectiveness of SCAN criteria in comparison to theoretically motivated indicators. Porter and Yuille describe a crime simulation study in which subjects created truthful accounts or alibis according to their role in the experiment. For their evaluation, the authors selected a subset of criteria from CBCA, RM, and SCAN. They found that all methods did poorly. Only three indicators, all from CBCA and all consistent with truthfulness, performed well: amount of detail, coherence, and lack of memory. Neither SCAN nor RM showed any usefulness for assessing veracity in this study.

However, there may be reasons other than doubtful criteria to explain the poor performance of RM and SCAN. Porter and Yuille [1996] point out that the two CBCA coders in their study were carefully trained, receiving "extensive 3-day training" (p. 449) in CBCA tagging. There is no reference to training or other preparation for RM and SCAN tagging. RM criteria were scored based on automated frequency counts of hedges (*I believe, It seems to me*, etc.), counts of self-references (*I, me, mine, my, myself*), and the word count of the entire narrative. SCAN criteria were scored based on automated frequency counts of "unnecessary connectors" (*afterwards, the next thing I remember*, etc.), a count of deviations from use of the first person singular pronoun

I (it is unclear if this was conducted manually or automatically) and statement balance (relative lengths of prologue and epilogue).

In the absence of an explicit description, it seems likely that all of the automated assignments were done with key word and key phrase searches. Pronoun deviations may also have been computationally assigned but details about the program or human involvement are not provided. This leaves open the question as to whether the program or a trained human rater identified first-person pronoun deviations. A shift from "I" to a different pronoun may indicate deception, as the authors observe, or it may simply serve to advance the narrative. For example, if the speaker says "I asked him where he was yesterday morning" and continues with "He replied that he was at home," the pronoun change from "I" to "he" fits the narrative flow. Trained human raters may recognize these different functions of pronoun change but it is unlikely that a keyword-based system could do so. In summary, the lack of sufficient training and the possible omission of context or critical words from automated key word/key phrase searches could have affected the RM and SCAN scores. The authors suggest as much: "It should be noted that none of the computer-generated measures discriminated among the groups. It is, of course, possible that a computational approach (computer or manually generated) was not a valid one in tapping the various variables being examined" [Porter and Yuille, 1996, p. 450]. It may be fair to say that the results reported in Porter and Yuille provide support for the winning CBCA criteria but are inconclusive with respect to the SCAN and RM criteria.

Nahari et al. [2012] compare the performance of a larger set of SCAN and RM criteria in a mock theft scenario. Subjects wrote narrative accounts that were later coded using 13 SCAN criteria from Vrij [2008] and 8 RM criteria from Sporer [2004]. Cue tagging was performed by 6 coders, each of whom received 90 min of training in SCAN and RM criteria. Each narrative account was tagged by two coders and disagreements as to whether an indicator was present or not were referred to a third coder who made the final decision. Low inter-rater reliability motivated the experimenters to adopt a simplified tagging scheme in which cues were deemed present or absent but information about tag frequency, which was part of the initial tagging scheme, was excluded. This improved rater performance but may have affected the scoring of SCAN criteria that make use of frequency, e.g., first-person pronouns.[3] Even so, inter-rater reliability is low to moderate (< .70) on some of the most important SCAN criteria—changes in pronoun use, structure of the statement and missing information. Results of the scoring showed RM succeeded in distinguishing liars from truth-tellers where SCAN failed to do so. However, the possibility exists that insufficient rater training, a simplified scoring system and rater disagreements may have played a role in SCAN's poor performance.

Finally, Nahari et al. [2012] make a strong argument for the value of RM's "theoretical underpinning." As a psychological model, RM holds the high ground compared to SCAN. A drawback of RM as a formal model, however, is that many of the criteria are impressionistic and

---

[3]From the SCAN workshop guidelines: "If we find only one (or two or three) first-person pronoun(s) (*I*, *we*) in the statement, the sentence(s) where they appear should be considered as very unique" (LSI SCAN workshop, 2004.)

refer to qualities such as "vibrancy," "richness," "clarity," and "realism" that people recognize but that are difficult to represent in an automated system. Many of the SCAN criteria, while lacking theoretical motivation, lend themselves to practical descriptions that work for instruction and implementation.[4]

Conclusion

The results obtained from laboratory tests of SCAN are at odds with those obtained from field studies. Both Driscoll [1994] and Adams and Jarvis [2006] found that statement balance, one of the most important SCAN criteria, figures significantly in discriminating truth and deception. The laboratory data studies failed to find any significant effect of statement balance. This should not be surprising since inconsistency across studies is prevalent among both laboratory research studies and field studies, whether they share a common framework and goals [Vrij, 2008] or are investigating competing frameworks [Nahari et al., 2012, Porter and Yuille, 1996] It would certainly prove productive to interpret inconsistencies as evidence of the need for more development of shared resources—data, software, training tools—and best practices. Such an effort would offer enormous benefits to field studies where assessments of ground truth are critical to producing reliable results.

---

[4][Bachenko et al., 2008] use several criteria borrowed from the statement analysis community, including SCAN.

CHAPTER 3

Data Sources

3.1 INTRODUCTION

As discussed in Chapter 2, particularly in reference to Reality Monitoring, the search for behavioral cues to deception is guided by the assumption that narratives based on experienced events differ in measurable ways from fabricated experiences. Laboratory experiments such as those considered in the previous chapter have produced a body of evidence indicating that several verbal and nonverbal behaviors correlate with fabricated accounts.

The scenarios used for laboratory experiments are often characterized as "low-stakes deception" because the subjects in these studies have little to lose if their lies are discovered. Most jurisdictions have regulations on the protection of human subjects that would prohibit experimental designs involving high-stakes situations. In a fabricated scenario, subjects are protected from any harm that might come from discovery of deception. Further, because subjects are instructed to lie, they need not take responsibility for the dishonest behavior: "In virtually every study of deceptive behavior, the researchers have sanctioned, even encouraged, the subjects' dishonest behavior, thus removing the onus of responsibility for the deception act from the deceiver and placing it on the researcher" [Koper and Sahlman, 1991, p. 2].

High-stakes deception in, for example, criminal cases, carries significant risk since discovery may have serious consequences for the deceiver and the deceiver's family, friends and colleagues. For many researchers and practitioners, the lack of ecological validity in low-stakes deception raises doubts about the ability of laboratory behaviors to stand for real-world deceptive behavior. It is possible that laboratory research has overlooked leakage behaviors in high-stakes deceivers since actual risk may promote behaviors that do not occur in low-stakes scenarios. It is also possible that laboratory tests overestimate the importance of certain behaviors that, in fact, have been linked to sanctioned deceit, as noted by Horvath et al. [1994], Vrij and Mann [2001a], and Fornaciari and Poesio [2013]. Questions about the validity of laboratory studies become a critical issue when we attempt to compare and evaluate theoretical models of deception and, equally important, when we attempt to build systems for the recognition of deceptive language by humans and machines.

Yet alternatives to laboratory-generated data have their own problems. The most important of these is the representation of ground truth. In a typical laboratory experiment, subjects are assigned to truthful or deceptive conditions and placed in scenarios where they describe their actions truthfully or deceptively depending on the role they have been assigned. The experimenters know the ground truth, i.e., which of the accounts is a lie and which is true, and can look for telltale behaviors under each condition. Ground truth for high-stakes situations is rarely as reliable or as well represented.

This chapter examines several "real-world" studies of language and deception. We begin with a brief description of data sources and go on to compare the different methods by which ground truth is established.

Current techniques for real-world deception studies are largely derived from methods developed for Criteria-Based Content Analysis (CBCA), discussed in Chapter 2, Section 2.4 as the language analysis component of Statement Validity Analysis (SVA). As we note there, CBCA was created to measure the veracity of child victims and witnesses in sexual assault cases. We have excluded real-world CBCA studies from our review for two reasons. First, Vrij's review of 37 real-world CBCA studies provides a thorough assessment of the history and effectiveness of CBCA techniques [Vrij, 2005]. Second, CBCA criteria in their original form depend on interpretive skills that would be difficult or impossible to represent in a NLP system. We thus forgo including the CBCA studies except to note that, as Vrij [2005] observes, CBCA research shares the critical challenges facing other efforts in real-world deception research: the availability of data and the verification of ground truth.

3.2   ESTABLISHING GROUND TRUTH

Establishing ground truth is the key to any investigation of behavioral cues to deception. When controlled by the experimenter, ground truth is unambiguous and accessible but when ground truth must be taken from an external source it is rarely free of uncertainty, especially in the case of forensic data. Despite the difficulties in establishing ground truth, a number of researchers have made use of data collected from sources outside the laboratory. The field studies reviewed in this chapter fall into three distinct categories according to their sources of linguistic data:[1]

- *legal and forensic interviews and statements:* police and prosecutor interviews, congressional testimony, courtroom proceedings;

- *financial reports:* earnings calls, corporate tax forms; and

- *mass media communications:* media interviews of high profile people and their aides and assistants.

With the exception of mass media communications, the task of collecting linguistic data can be surprisingly difficult [Fitzpatrick and Bachenko, 2010, 2012]. Fitzpatrick and Bachenko [2012] cover public sources for this data, including crime investigation websites, published police interviews, legal websites such as findlaw.com and justice.gov, quarterly earnings conference calls, and the U.S. Congressional Record.

---

[1]Issues related to a fourth category, product reviews, are covered in Chapters 4 and 5 since the collection and annotation of product review data is integral to specific computational approaches.

Data must be limited to what can be verified by ground truth sources, and researchers are bound by ethical constraints established, in the U.S., by Institutional Review Boards (IRBs) and by similar bodies in other countries.[2]

In addition, we have found that nearly all the data available for real-world deception research comes from people who have been shown to be (or are assumed to be) guilty of wrongdoing, either criminal or civil, or social in the case of media celebrities. Comparable language data from innocent people is rare.

3.2.1   FORENSIC DATA SOURCES: SPOKEN AND WRITTEN

Forensic data for spoken productions comes from transcripts of recorded interviews and court proceedings. Corpus sizes are small by machine learning standards, ranging from six utterances[3] by a single speaker [Vrij and Mann, 2001a] to over 3,000 utterances by 31 speakers in the DeCour corpus [Fornaciari and Poesio, 2013].

Although limited in scope, Vrij and Mann [2001a] was an influential early study that articulated an approach to data collection and ground truth estimation that has been used in later studies. Researchers manually examined verbatim transcripts of video recordings of a single criminal suspect later convicted of murder. Only clips that could be verified as true or false were admitted into the corpus: three lies and three truthful segments ranging in duration from 16–67 s. Comparisons of the utterances yielded some evidence of differences in vocal and nonverbal behaviors—lies occurred with longer pauses, a slower speaking rate and more disfluencies—but the small dataset is insufficient to support any solid conclusions. In a follow-up study, Mann et al. [2002] extended the data set to videos of 16 criminal suspects, only some of whom were convicted. Using the same corpus construction method employed by Vrij and Mann [2001a], the final corpus comprised 65 verifiable utterances: 27 truthful utterances and 38 lies ranging in duration from 5.2–145.7 s. Comparisons of the true and false utterances indicated that "suspects blinked less and paused longer while lying" [Mann et al., 2002, p. 371]. The authors acknowledge, however, that the limited availability of language data and the work effort required to make it usable prevented them from drawing from a larger subject pool that might have yielded richer results.

Continuing on the path set by Vrij and Mann [2001a], Davis et al. [2005] explore the interaction between deception, truth telling, and the incriminating potential of a question or

---

[2]Fitzpatrick and Bachenko [2012] provide a detailed account of the types of linguistic data and ground truth sources that are consistent with the requirements of ethics committees. The most significant constraint for most real-world deception studies is the subject's expectation of privacy, which limits data sources to high profile individuals, convicted criminals, public figures, and the deceased. A subject's right to privacy is recognized by the ethics agreements of many, but not all, countries. (http://www.hhs.gov/ohrp/international/intlcompilation/intlcompilation.html).

[3]The definition of utterance varies across studies. Vrij and Mann [2001a] define an utterance (which they term a "fragment," p. 191) as a span of transcribed speech that can be verified as true or false. The utterances defined by Vrij and Mann are video clips of the suspect "where truth or lie had been strongly supported by other convincing evidence" [Mann et al., 2002, p. 368]. It does not appear that utterances in these studies are limited to individual propositions or sentences. In Fornaciari and Poesio [2013] utterances are identified in transcriptions of the defendant's speech as "strings of text delimited by punctuation marks, such as periods, question marks, and ellipses." Davis et al. [2005] describe an utterance as a spoken answer that contains up to three pieces of information that must pertain to the topic under scrutiny and be capable of corroboration.

statement. Their data source consists of recorded confessions by 28 criminal suspects who were eventually convicted. The suspects were filmed giving their confessions to an assistant district attorney after the police interview. As with the previous two studies, researchers examined verbatim transcriptions of the videos. They identified 337 utterances that could be confirmed as true or false; utterance durations ranged from 0.15–41.6 s, and utterance word counts ranged from 1–66. The experimenters found evidence for some cues to deception, e.g., word repetition and the phrase "I don't know" but also identified non-verbal cues for stress, e.g., speaking rate, that did not discriminate truth from deception but may be indicative of incriminating content in an utterance. With respect to their data source, the authors express strong reservations about the guilt bias in their corpus: "we cannot assess the extent to which our results were skewed because we could only obtain tapes of subjects judged guilty. We would expect the behavior of a guilty suspect who confessed for personal gain, psychological need or compliance-with-authority motives to be very different from the behavior of an innocent suspect who was coerced or psychologically motivated to make a false confession" [Davis et al., 2005, p. 700].

Automated, or partially automated, approaches are described by Fornaciari and Poesio [2013] and Bachenko et al. [2008]. Both have developed corpora based on transcribed narratives from several speakers. The Italian DeCour corpus [Fornaciari and Poesio, 2013] comprises transcriptions of Italian court hearings for judgment on perjury cases. The corpus is substantial, consisting of 35 hearings from four Italian courts and 31 different people. The corpus developed by Bachenko et al. is made up of several statements by people implicated in a variety of civil and criminal activities. These include police interviews, lawsuit depositions, and congressional testimony totaling slightly over 30,000 words.

Three published studies have assembled and analyzed collections of written statements by criminal suspects and victims. Driscoll [1994] examined 30 statements prepared by criminal suspects prior to a polygraph examination. Smith [2001] conducted experiments using 27 criminal statements provided by U.S. law enforcement groups. Adams and Jarvis [2006] investigated 60 statements produced by adult suspects and victims during criminal investigations, as described in more detail in Chapter 2, Section 2.4, in the presentation of statement analysis.

3.2.2   FINANCIAL REPORTS

In contrast with forensic venues, data sources for financial reporting, at least within the U.S., are easily found for publicly traded companies (companies that offer stocks for sale). Transcripts of earnings calls and Form 10-Ks are public documents available through the Securities and Exchange Commission (www.sec.gov/edgar.shtml) and a number of web-based sources. Earnings conference calls typically open with a report on the company's financial performance and then move on to a question and answer (Q/A) session, with the Chief Executive Officer (CEO) and Chief Financial Officer (CFO) answering unrehearsed questions from analysts, investors, and media representatives. Fraud occurs when a financial statement presents information that is incorrect or misleading. In such cases the report must be revised and published as a restatement. There are verification issues with the use of these restatements, as discussed in Section 3.2.1.

Two recent studies have compared the language of statements and restatements in an effort to develop predictive models of fraud in earnings call Q/As. Larcker and Zakolyukina [2010] obtained earnings call transcripts from FactSet Research Systems Inc. The transcribed corpus represented a diverse collection of public companies: "We consider all available transcripts of quarterly earnings conference calls for the U.S. companies over the time period from 2003 to 2007" [Larcker and Zakolyukina, 2010, p. 12]. Of the 31,039 answer narratives—a "narrative" being the turn taken in answer to a question on a call—that make up Larcker and Zakolyukina's corpus, 10% were judged deceptive based on the reclassification of certain reports as restatements.

In an exploratory study, Burgoon et al. limit their data source to earnings calls from a single company [Burgoon et al., 2015]. Their corpus consists of 1,114 sentences (Burgoon et al's "utterances") derived from transcripts made available by Thomson Reuters StreetEvents (www.st reetevents.com). Like Larcker and Zakolyukina, Burgoon et al. attempt to identify linguistic indicators of deception in the language of the earnings call Q/A. Their approach differs from that of Larcker and Zakolyukina in that (i) their primary unit of analysis is the sentence and (ii) they use both vocal and linguistic cues to identify deception in the statement, as compared to the psychologocially motivated Linguistic Inquiry and Word Count (LIWC) features used by Larcker and Zakolyukina. The limit on corpus size comes largely from the significant investment in time and labor to identify and analyze sentences in the speech that can be verified as T or F, and to verify the sentences as related or unrelated to the restatement.

A related study by Humpherys et al. [2011] examines deceptive language in the Form 10-K, which is a required annual report for publicly traded companies in the U.S. (http://www.sec.gov/answers/reada10k.htm). Similar to the earnings report calls, Form 10-K contains a section—Management's Discussion and Analysis (MD&A)—where management can discuss the company's financial health, operations, and market risks. It is this section that Humpherys et al. believe can be analyzed for evidence of management fraud. Cases of known fraud in the 10-K are available from the SEC, making it possible for Humphreys et al. to build a corpus relatively easily of 101 fraudulent 10-K's and 101 "comparable non-fraudulent 10-K's" [Humpherys et al., 2011, p. 589], where each MD&A was analyzed for a set of linguistic indicators selected by the authors.

The relative ease of obtaining speech and language data in financial reporting make this an accessible and promising area for deception studies. Issues concerning ground truth, discussed below, present significant hurdles but are perhaps less complex than those associated with forensic studies.

3.2.3 MASS MEDIA COMMUNICATIONS

Koper and Sahlman [1991] examine TV interviews of high profile Americans and their closest aides and assistants. In many ways, this is an ideal data source since the data is readily available and, by appearing on television, subjects relinquish any expectation of privacy and are highly motivated to cultivate "an image of honesty" [Koper and Sahlman, 1991, p. 16]. Statements in the videos were revealed to be deceptive either by the subject's subsequent admission or by incriminating evidence.

To build their corpus, Koper and Sahlman purchased 165 videos from the TV news archive at Vanderbilt University. A sample of the subject pool includes Pete Rose, Gary Hart, Richard Nixon, Oliver North, and Zsa Zsa Gabor. Two raters coded the videos for several visual, vocal and language cues that had been identified in earlier studies as leakage conduits, e.g., blaming, excuses, lack of directness and lack of plausibility. Results of the analysis were mixed. While no cue or set of cues stands out strongly, the authors found that deceptive portions of the interviewee's speech did reveal verbal leakage behaviors that included less directness, less consistency, and less plausibility. This result seems surprising since few of the spoken excerpts were spontaneous—most of the lies in the videos were planned—but it suggests that speeches and interviews of high profile speakers may offer an accessible and productive source of linguistic data.

3.3   RISKS WITH GROUND TRUTH SOURCES

There is no ground truth standard for the data sources we have described. Researchers employ a variety of ground truth criteria depending on the data's origins. Moreover, absolute ground truth may be impossible to establish in some cases, especially with forensic data [Driscoll, 1994]. False confession, an acquittal on appeal, mistrials, and false testimony can and do occur, making decisions of guilt or innocence probabilistic rather than absolute. Hence, it is often necessary to accept a degree of uncertainty in ground truth judgments, particularly for forensic data sources.

Fornaciari and Poesio [2013] make this point in their examination of ground truth criteria for the DeCour corpus. The basic unit of analysis in DeCour is the utterance: "strings of text delimited by punctuation marks," and limited to the defendant's speech. Verification of an utterance as true or false is based on the court transcription, which contains both a verbatim record of the defendant's speech and the court's assessment of certain responses as lies or truth. Researchers manually tagged the defendants' utterances as True, False, or Uncertain. The Uncertain tag was assigned if truthfulness of an utterance could not be satisfactorily determined or if it lacked propositional content, e.g., "May you repeat, please?" Inter-rater reliability was .64 on 600 utterances when the tagging task consisted of a binary classification of utterances as False vs. Not-false, with Not-false comprising True and Uncertain. With respect to verification, Fornaciari and Poesio [2013] caution that an element of ground truth error is unavoidable: "how confident can we be that the statements marked as false are actually false? Of course, it is possible that court judgments are wrong: some evidence coming from the inquiry could be in some way mistaken or misinterpreted by the judge. Since the annotation of DeCour relies on the information provided by the judgment, this would bring about an erroneous evaluation of the statements' truthfulness and would result in some noise in the data. This kind of risk is unavoidable."

Table 3.1: Driscoll [1994, p. 82] criteria for rendering a T/F judgment of an entire statement

Doubtful Statement (likely deceptive)	Apparently Accurate (likely truthful)
1. confession by subject	confession by another person
2. arrest of subject	arrest of another person
3. conviction of subject	conviction of another person
4. deceptive polygraph	truthful polygraph
5. case dropped by police (applies to victims' statements only)	case pursued by police (victims only)

3.3.1   LEGAL AND FORENSIC INTERVIEWS AND STATEMENTS

The risk of ground truth error is probably greatest in analyses of criminal interviews such as those described by Vrij and Mann [2001a], Mann et al. [2002], Davis et al. [2005], Adams and Jarvis [2006], and Bachenko et al. [2008]. These studies depend on ground truth verification that is based on the evidence collected in the course of the investigation and, in some studies, the subject's consistency or contradiction in the repetition of the facts to be verified. To classify utterances as true or false, Vrij and Mann [2001a] and Mann et al. [2002] relied on physical evidence (e.g., hair, fibers), recanted statements (denying guilt and then admitting it), statements by witnesses close to the case and statements by co-offenders implicated in the crime. The Davis experimenters worked with detectives to identify transcribed utterances containing verifiable propositions. Information from the investigation and criminal records was then used to validate propositions as true or false, including laboratory evidence, crime scene analysis and accounts by witnesses and suspects. In Bachenko et al. [2008] researchers identified propositions that could be verified using a set of criteria that excluded descriptions of mental states such as "I think," "as far as I know," and "I don't remember." Verification was determined by evidence based on crime scene videos, police reports, court documents, corporate records and recanted statements. As in most studies, subjects in each of these were judged to be guilty of wrongdoing.

Adams and Jarvis [2006] use ground truth criteria along the same lines as other studies: "conviction of the subject by a judge or jury, overwhelming physical case evidence, or corroborated confession by the offender" [Adams and Jarvis, 2006, p. 12]. Unfortunately, such descriptions of ground truth resources are quite vague. It is difficult to replicate precisely a set of ground truth criteria that meet standards expressed as "substantial reliable independent witness" [Mann et al., 2002, p. 368], or witnesses with "close up and fairly protracted exposure to the criminal activity" [Davis et al., 2005, p. 689].

Driscoll [1994] and Smith [2001] list explicit criteria for judging an entire statement as true or false based on the outcome of the criminal investigation. In both studies, assignment to the "likely deceptive" or "likely truthful" category occurred when at least two criteria of a category were met. Driscoll's criteria are summarized in Table 3.1.

Smith [2001, p. 31] replaces Driscoll's criteria 4 and 5 with the following:

- Truthful criterion: Unequivocal evidence to support the truth of the statement

- Deceptive criterion: Unequivocal evidence to support the deceit within the statement

Smith is unclear about the source of ground truth corroboration, saying only that "The statements were originally classified by the U.S. police as 'true', 'deceitful' or 'inconclusive' .... Inconclusive statements were categorized as those that possessed only one, if any, of these criteria" [Smith, 2001, p. 31]. Clearly there is a need in forensic research for ground truth standards that identify preferred sources of validation along with heuristics for weighting the probability of error in ground truth determination. Even so it is possible that although ground truth corpora tend to be small they are sufficient to support behavioral studies of truth and deception. Table 3.2 summarizes the ground truth corpus size for the forensic studies discussed above.

Table 3.2: Counts of ground truth units

Type of GT unit	Source	Count of ground truth units			
		Total	True	False	Uncertain
Written Statements	Driscoll (1994)	30	11	19	
	Smith (2001)	27	4	20	3
	Adams and Jarvis (2006)	60	30	30	—
Utterances	Vrij and Mann (2001)	6	3	3	
	Mann et al. (2002)	65	27	38	
	Fornaciari and Poesio (2013)	3015	1202	945	868
	Davis et al. (2005)	337	229	108	
Propositions	Bachenko et al. (2008)	275	111	164	

3.3.2   FINANCIAL REPORTS

As with data collection, ground truth for financial reports is considerably more accessible than data for forensic and related domains. Public resources and private companies can be used to identify fraudulent reporting and obtain statements and other documents. For example, the U.S. Securities and Exchange Commission produces Accounting and Auditing Enforcement Releases (AAERs) that provide information uncovered during the investigation of a company for financial misconduct. Humpherys et al. [2011] relied on AAERs to identify a set of fraud cases that involved Form 10-Ks. The original Form 10-Ks that AAERs showed to be fraudulent were used to build the deceptive corpus. The truthful corpus was built from cases where there was no indication of fraud. In the case of restatements and fraud, restatement databases are maintained by the Government Accountability Office and a number of private companies. Larcker and Zakolyukina [2010] used Glass, Lewis & Co. to identify restatements that they used in constructing their corpus of deceptive reports.

Several pieces of evidence may go into a fraud investigation and be used to establish ground truth. The company selected for Burgoon et al. [2015] analysis submitted a restatement to correct the overstated earnings given in the original statement. In addition, several class action suits were filed against the CEO and CFO and settled in favor of the plaintiffs, the allegations against the CEO and CFO led to their leaving the company and the SEC started an investigation. Larcker and Zakolyukina [2010] label a restatement narrative deceptive only if "they involve substantial subsequent restatement or net income and are associated with more severe types of restatements such as the disclosure of a material weakness, the change of an auditor, a late filing, or a Form 8-K filing" (pp. 2-3).

These criteria are convincing but they do not guarantee the validity of ground truth. Detailed information about the fraud—exactly how it was perpetrated—may not be publicly available. It is possible that lawsuits, later restatements and new discoveries will alter ground truth. In addition, we cannot always know if executives were aware of the deception: "executives may not know about the manipulation at the time of the conference call" [Larcker and Zakolyukina, 2010, p. 34]. Personal communications and conflicting financial statements may reveal what executives knew but without direct evidence it is rarely possible to ascertain state of mind. More studies are needed in this promising area in order to develop a clear and possibly ranked set of ground truth standards.

3.3.3 MASS MEDIA COMMUNICATIONS

The availability of ground truth as well as spoken data offers a strong argument for expanding formal studies of deception cues to data derived from mass media communications. Koper and Sahlman [1991] performed their study before the current era of ubiquitous media and fact checking resources. The constant presence of high profile speakers on radio, TV, and the internet, and the existence of organizations such as FactCheck.org and PolitiFact.com have created a fundamental change in the accessibility of language data and ground truth verification. Development of this venue could solve many of the data and ground truth issues that make large deception corpora so difficult to construct.

CHAPTER 4

The Language of Deception: Computational Approaches

4.1 COMPUTATIONAL APPROACHES TO VERBAL DECEPTION

This chapter reviews the NLP studies on the automatic detection of deception that present a predictive model of deceptive verbal productions. As such, the studies have the characteristics of applied work in the NLP community, including:

- the use of comparative measures of system performance;

- the use of a classification scheme to separate the true from the deceptive productions or a ranking scheme to estimate the likelihood of a production being deceptive;

- training on a portion of the data and testing on the remainder, often entailing cross-validation due to the small size of many datasets in deception work; and

- the use of one or more evaluation measures to measure success and enable comparison across systems.

Many studies also involve significant data preparation, primarily including tokenization and stemming.

4.1.1 ESTABLISHING COMPARATIVE MEASURES OF SYSTEM PERFORMANCE

Accuracy in predicting whether a narrative is T(rue) or F(alse) is the most common measure of performance in NLP deception research, so we need to consider what level of accuracy is good. Is 80% accuracy good or bad? Good as compared to what?

Ideally, to evaluate a classification system we have to compare it to an entity that performs the same task on the same data. To demonstrate high performance, the system should perform significantly better than the current ceiling, or upper-bound level of performance. For many NLP tasks, the ceiling is human performance. Marcus et al. [1993], for example, cite humans as agreeing on 96–97% of the tags in the Penn Treebank version of the Brown corpus. However, in deception research, human performance is often cited as the baseline, or lower-bound, since human performance in determining whether someone is lying or not, is notoriously low, with average accuracy scores of 50%, [Bond and Paulo, 2006, Ekman and O'Sullivan, 1991]. The earliest deception work in the NLP paradigm had no other figure to compare to, and so cited this randomness in human ability to spot a liar as a type of performance that could be improved upon.

At this point in deception research, however, this approach is no longer tenable. More recent research has shown that there is a wide range of skills among humans, and humans with experience in detecting deception perform better [Ekman et al., 1999, Mann et al., 2004, Vrij and Mann, 2001b]. More importantly, the data for a given experiment may be quite different from the experiments that found the chance findings. For NLP applications, a more reliable baseline may be determined by using human judges in the same experiment that is testing the automatic detection system. This approach was taken by Newman et al. [2003], which found their human judges correctly classifying 52% of the narratives in one of their five narrative tasks, and Ott et al. [2011], which found a majority accuracy of 58% among its three human judges estimating T/F on the same hotel reviews as did their automatic system.

Another approach considers the baseline to be the balance of T and F narratives; if there are 50 true narratives, for example, and 50 false narratives, then the baseline is considered to be 50%. This approach is taken by Mihalcea and Strapparava [2009].

As for a ceiling against which to compare, the field is now providing prior experiments on the same data thanks to hotel opinion spam data made publicly available by Myle Ott.[1] Ott et al.'s published results [Ott et al., 2011, 2013] have been used as the ceiling, or best practice, against which to compare subsequent systems.[2] This chapter covers several papers using the Ott hotel data and referencing the Ott et al. [2011] results. Of course, expanding to other data sets—even review data of a different type, such as the Amazon book review data of Fornaciari and Poesio [2014]—will require a new baseline and establish a new ceiling.

4.1.2   CLASSIFICATION AND RANKING

The task of separating true from false narratives is most often viewed as a binary classification task although, depending on the application, it may be viewed as a task estimating the likelihood of deception. Most of the applications covered here involve supervised learning, using a training set of narratives each of which is known to be a member of either the T or F class. Thus, the most commonly used implementation algorithms are the Naïve Bayes classifier and the Support Vector Machine classifier.

Several mathematical models have been put to the service of this task, with input to the classifiers at linguistic levels from the character and n-gram up to and including the discourse structure. Zhou et al. [2004b] compares the results of four mathematical models—discriminant analysis, logistic regression, decision trees, and neural networks—on an email communication

---

[1]http://myleott.com/op_spam/
[2]Some of the papers covered in this chapter use the term "baseline" simply to mean "system against which to compare" rather than lower-bound.

task. The study shows high overall accuracy rates of around 80% for logistic regression and neural networks.

4.1.3   TRAINING AND TESTING

A standard method of training a language model is by cross-validation (CV) in which a large portion of the data, as much as 90%, is used to train the model and the remaining portion is held out for testing. This is usually done multiple times, or folds, so that all of the data gets to be used for training and all for testing, as in "5-fold" or "10-fold" cross-validation.

Many of the deception studies vary the contextual features of the narratives, primarily in terms of narrative topic. Some studies use data from the full variety of narratives for training and testing. The more challenging train/test protocol in this situation is to hold out one narrative topic from training to use for testing. The aim of this type of testing is to see how generalizable are the features that are being used to discriminate truthful from deceptive narratives. Newman et al. [2003], for example, create a particularly challenging task by including five narrative types that vary in either topic or mode (abortion (video, typed, or written), friends (video), mock crime (video)) and testing on each one using the data from the other four as the training set. As we will see below, their accuracy rates are significantly better when the topic in the testing occurs in the training also.

4.1.4   SYSTEM EVALUATION

Table 4.1: A confusion matrix for deception

		Predicted Class	
		True	False
Actual Class	True	A	B
	False	C	D

Given the confusion matrix in Table 4.1, where the rows correspond to the known class of the data, i.e., the labels T and F obtained from the ground truth data and the columns correspond to the predictions made by the model, there are several standard evaluation measures, listed below, that can be obtained. Accuracy is an estimate of the success of a model in discriminating True from False narratives; the other measures are used to evaluate the success of a model in determining True narratives or False narratives.[3]

Accuracy is a measure of the narratives that are correctly classified (A+D)/(A+B+C+D).

---

[3]If only one figure is reported, it is most commonly a measure of the False documents since most applications are concerned with identifying the deceptive communications.

False Positive is a measure of the True narratives that are classified as False: C/(A+C), or False narratives that are classified as True: B/(C+D).

Precision is a measure of actual True narratives that are predicted True: A/(A+C), or of actual False narratives that are predicted False: D/(B+D).

Recall[4] is a measure of the actual Trues that were found by the system: A/(A+B), or of the actual False narratives that were found: D/(C+D).

F-measure: the harmonic mean of precision and recall
(2 * (precision * recall)/precision + recall)).

The measure used should be dependent on the application. Accuracy is the most commonly used measure in deception classification since most applications aim to give equal importance to the True and the False identification. But there are applications that need to find false statements at the expense of overtagging trues as false—electronic communications that might signal criminal activity, for example. In such cases, a high recall value is important.

Given the diversity of the narratives being classified as T/F by current systems from 140 character tweets to hours long spoken testimony and the purpose of each application, where high false positives might be more or less costly, it is impossible to pick a best approach. However, the evaluation measures give some ability to compare systems, keeping in mind the extreme diversity of the applications; for this reason, recent studies often provide multiple measures.

4.1.5   PREPPING THE DATA

Among the tools used to prepare data for experimentation, a stop-list is not usually used when preparing data for T/F classification. While the function words usually included on a stop-list are thought to carry little semantic weight, the distinction between self/group-referencing pronouns and possessives (I, me, my, we, etc.) and other-referencing pronouns and possessives ($you, your, she, them$, etc.) is considered critical in much deception work, as are modal verbs, which can express uncertainty, and prepositions, which can capture spatio-temporal relations or function as the head of an embedded sentence, as do $because, although$, etc.

Stemming, in which morphological variants are reduced to a single form, is also sometimes avoided. Depending on the T/F discrimination model, voice, tense, and aspect may be considered discriminators.

Again, depending on the deception model, the data may also be tagged for part-of-speech and/or parsed.

4.2   CONSIDERATIONS SPECIFIC TO DECEPTION

There are several types of variation in the data that are common to many NLP applications and that are particularly relevant to deception studies. These include variation in the types of data to

---

[4]Also referred to as Detection Rate.

be analyzed, the unit of analysis that is classified as true or deceptive, the attempt to characterize lies of omission as well as commission, the topic, and, of course, the linguistic level of the data, which can range from the character up to the structure of the discourse. In addition, there are issues peculiar to deception studies that involve how ground truth is obtained and recorded.

4.2.1   DATA TYPES AMENABLE TO DECEPTION RESEARCH

There are many domains and genres in which high-stakes lying can be found. The choice of data types to model and test is only moderately constrained by the narrative's ability to display deception and the needs of NLP modeling and testing. Assuming that liars leak cues to their deception, narratives that are rehearsed, such as public speeches, put the behaviors of the narrator, particularly language choices, under conscious control; so narrative data needs to be spontaneous or semi-spontaneous. This is possible even for written narratives under certain conditions. In addition, the data needs to have more language to be analyzed than the simple "Yes/No" responses of, for example, a polygraph test. Finally, in order to test an NLP deception model, the data or portions of the data have to be verifiable. Issues of verifiability are covered in Chapter 3, Section 3.2 and in Fitzpatrick and Bachenko [2012].

Communications that involve both substantial narrative portions and the possibility of deception can be divided across two dimensions, interactivity and elicitation.[5] Dialogues may either be interactive, in which case the narrative is constructed by all involved parties, or it can be non-interactive, constructed by one narrator for an audience of one or more, as in the case of a lecture, a webpage, or unsolicited email.

The second dimension, elicitation, captures whether the narrator is being asked to provide the narrative or is giving it freely. The narrator has less control over an elicited narrative, possibly increasing the odds for the appearance of cues to deception.

Table 4.2 shows the possible venues, classified according to interactivity and elicitation, in which spontaneous or semi-spontaneous communication, and therefore substantial deception, can occur. We exclude certain data types because such data is not publicly available, its veracity cannot be ascertained, or human subject issues make it impossible to use. Fitzpatrick and Bachenko [2012] cover these issues in detail.

4.2.2   UNIT OF ANALYSIS: THE LIAR OR THE LIE

Some applications seek to classify the narrator as a liar or a truth-teller based on the full narrative, which means that the classification scheme will operate on the full text rather than on individual propositions. Other applications seek to classify individual propositions or perhaps a group of propositions as a lie, with other claims classified as either truthful or unknown with respect to deception.

The particular application may demand one level rather than the other; for example, for online hotel reviews [Ott et al., 2011], the reader wants to know whether the review was actually

---

[5]These dimensions and the basis for Table 4.2 are from [Burgoon et al., 2004].

Table 4.2: Venues of verbal deception; dotted lines separate spoken from written language

	Interactive	Not Interactive
Elicited	Face-to-face Depositions Court testimony Other public testimony Phone conversations — — — — — — — - Chat/email	Recorded statements to police — — — — — — — - Written statements to police
Not Elicited	Overhearing Wiretap — — — — — — — - Chat/email	Voicemail Recorded speech Political speeches — — — — — — — - Online product endorsements Unsolicited email Facebook Other social media Webpages

written by someone who stayed at the hotel, rather than whether each claim is entirely valid. Ott et al.'s [2011] reviews are short, averaging 115 words, so the difference between determining the liar and the lie is minimal.

A longer narrative such as occurs in investigative interviews or trial testimony may have a mix of truthful statements and fabrications. In such cases fact finding is dependent on the individual claims and so the lies in the narrative need to be identified rather than the overall veracity of the narrator. Longer narratives also present the opportunity to observe the linguistic behavior of the narrator and idiosyncrasies s/he may exhibit in lying.

4.2.3   LIES OF OMISSION AND COMMISSION

Most of the work done in deception detection deals with lies of commission, where the liar makes claims that are not true. As we have seen throughout, the expectation in such cases is that the language of the lie will be different from the language used in the relay of a truth. However, the narrator may tell a story in which critical facts are simply omitted from the telling. For example, Scott Peterson, convicted of murdering his pregnant wife in California in 2002, describes in detail his boat trip to an island on the day his wife went missing, but fails to mention that her body was in the boat and that he left it on the island. Other than the dropping of first person pronouns, there is no significant difference between his language use in this description and his language use when detailing facts about himself, his house, etc. Omission is generally harder to identify. For one thing, the narrator is making no claim; he is only neglecting to include all relevant information.

4.2.4 LEVEL OF DATA USED FOR MODELING

The linguistic level at which the data is analyzed in recent NLP studies ranges from that of the character to that of the structure of the discourse, with most studies using either the *n*-gram or lexical features that have been shown by the prior literature on deception to be relevant.

4.2.5 TRAINING DATA AND GROUND TRUTH

All work in deception must deal with the ground truth problem. To be able to recognize the lie, the researcher must not only identify distinctive behavior when someone is lying but must ascertain whether the statement being made is true or not in order to assess the accuracy of the classification.

As discussed in Section 3.1, the standard method of obtaining ground truth is through a laboratory experiment where subjects can report their lies or be filmed committing the acts that they subsequently lie about. The most common alternative to the laboratory experiment is fact checking after the narrative has been produced. Either method yields a small amount of verified data, so a standard *n*-gram bag-of-words approach over millions of words of narrative is not possible. To get around the small dataset problem, most systems resort to a more abstract level of analysis than the *n*-gram. Many systems use features that prior psychology and/or criminal justice research have shown to be correlated with deception. We examine these features as well as other current NLP approaches to deception detection below.

4.3 THE CURRENT SYSTEMS

Deception detection is a relatively new application in computational linguistics, with most of the work appearing in the last ten years. In that decade, however, several groups have produced more than one publication in the area, in which case we concentrate on the seminal publication for the group unless other publications are substantially different in terms either of the application or the methods used to identify false narratives.

The systems covered here conform to the characteristics of applied work in NLP—use of a baseline, a classification scheme, a training/testing protocol, and one or more of the standard evaluation metrics. This not only puts the work squarely in the NLP framework, but it enables us to make what we hope to be useful comparisons.

The coverage is organized by the level at which the model is built, starting with the character and *n*-gram through the lexical feature and syntactic structure and up to the logical and discourse structures.

4.3.1   CHARACTERS AND *n*-GRAMS

At the smallest level of analysis is the character, an appropriate level of analysis for short narratives like tweets, for which Chen et al. [2014] have built a system to detect scamming tweets of three types:[6]

1. straight cons, which seek to get money from users through "Easy-money, work-from-home" schemes or "money-making with Twitter" scams;

2. twitomercials, which send users to a fake site where they are asked to pay a shipping fee for a bogus product or service; and

3. phishing and virus spreading scams, which deceive users into entering passwords, etc. and use these to phish or to spread a virus.

Chen et al. uses a suffix tree algorithm for classification. Suffix trees allow fast implementation, but require considerably more space than storing the string itself, and so may not be appropriate for longer narratives. To build their dataset, Chen et al. [2014] collected 9,296 unique tweets by querying for frequent English stop words and phrases known to occur in scam tweets, such as "work at home" and "teeth whitening." 40% of these tweets were randomly assigned to the test set, which was labeled independently by the three researchers and checked for inter-rater reliability. Nine tweets in the training set were also labeled. The training set was subjected to model-based clustering to ensure that the three scam types and the non-scam tweets would be highly differentiated. Each tweet was then iteratively included into the training set as scam or non-scam based on its match with each class.

Chen et al. report an accuracy rate of 70.39%, which, after self-training on the 4,000 unlabeled training tweets, increased to 87%. The dataset that Chen et al. are able to produce with their semi-supervised method is extremely large by deception detection standards. The lack of wide variation in the data makes their approach feasible. As the description of the three scam types above shows, there is a common set of words that each set shares with the other members of the set. For applications where the False and/or True data has this characteristic, a semi-supervised method can produce a large dataset, making an analysis at the level of the character feasible.

At the level of the *n*-gram, Mihalcea and Strapparava [2009] (**M&S**)[7] tested the extent to which the text in 300 false narratives can be automatically distinguished from that in 300 true narratives on three widely varying topics. They gave the topics to 100 Mechanical Turkers with instructions to write a 4–5 sentence narrative about their true feelings and the contrary on each topic. Tokenization and stemming were performed on the narratives; stopwords were not eliminated. Table 4.3 shows the cross-topic accuracy results achieved by M&S using Naïve Bayes (NB) and Support Vector Machine (SVM) classifiers with 10-fold cross-validation for testing.

---

[6]There is a great deal of research on assessing information credibility on the web using factors external to the narrative, including information sources, proportion of dubious messages, distortion of ratings based on messages, etc. A good source for this research are the WebQuality workshops associated with the annual International World Wide Web Conference.

[7]We have assigned the articles that will be discussed in several places throughout this chapter abbreviated names, e.g., "M&S" for Mihalcea and Strapparava, to facilitate referencing.

Table 4.3: Mihalcea and Strapparava's T/F classification accuracy (%)

Topic	NB	SVM
ABORTION	70.0	67.5
DEATH PENALTY	67.4	65.9
BEST FRIEND	75.0	70.1
AVERAGE	70.8	70.1

With the baseline for this study at 50%, given the balance of 300 true and 300 false narratives, these results are significant, demonstrating the promise of automatic classification in distinguishing two types of language.

M&S also test the effect of topic on the classification results, using the data from two of the topics for training, with testing done on the remaining topic. Table 4.4 shows the effect of topic change on the success of the classification, with accuracy cut in half or more. This is not surprising given expected differences in the words (*n*-grams) used to discuss each of the topics.

Table 4.4: Mihalcea and Strapparava's cross-topic accuracy (%)

Training	Test	NB	SVM
DEATH PENALTY + BEST FRIEND	ABORTION	62.0	61.0
ABORTION + BEST FRIEND	DEATH PENALTY	58.7	58.7
ABORTION + DEATH PENALTY	BEST FRIEND	58.7	53.6
AVERAGE		59.8	57.8

In a post hoc study, M&S also consider the effectiveness of the class-based features of Linguistic Inquiry and Word Count (LIWC), discussed below, by ranking the five LIWC features that appear most often in their deceptive narratives and least often in their true narratives and vice-versa. For example, the LIWC feature which most greatly distanced the deceptive text from the truthful text was "METAPHYSICAL," which included the words *god, die, sacred, mercy, sin, dead, hell, soul, lord, sins*, while the LIWC feature that distanced the truthful from the deceptive text was "OPTIMISM," which included the words *best, ready, hope, accept, accepted, determined, accepted, won, super*.

M&S established that it is possible to differentiate lexically diverse true from deceptive narratives at the *n*-gram level with a degree of significance while Chen et al., having picked a highly tractable narrative application with little lexical variation, showed that the differentiation can be accomplished with a high degree of success at the level of the character. Other studies have continued to use the *n*-gram level, primarily as a baseline against which to compare models using more abstract representations of the data, including LIWC and other features.

Ott et al. [2011] (**Ott**), also testing the ability of n-grams as well as part-of-speech (POS) tag frequencies and LIWC features to discriminate T from F narratives, are able to achieve a remarkable level of discrimination on 4–5 sentence hotel reviews of Chicago hotels. The Ott data is different in several ways. The 400 false narratives are clearly false; Mechanical Turkers wrote them. Each Turker was given the name and website of the hotel s/he was to review and told to pretend to work for the hotel's marketing department and produce a realistic, favorable review. The authors take several steps to retrieve a comparable number of true reviews, mining almost 7,000 reviews from TripAdvisor[8] of the 20 most popular hotels and eliminating non-5-star reviews (assumedly for parity with the glowing false reviews), non-English reviews, short reviews, and reviews written by first-time authors since this is not the typical TripAdvisor pattern. Table 4.5 shows the Ott results on the n-gram models using Naïve Bayes and Support Vector Machine classifiers and a 5-fold nested CV procedure that evaluates learned models on reviews from unseen hotels.

Table 4.5: Ott's n-gram accuracy (%). The + indicates that the feature set subsumes the preceding feature set. [Ott et al., 2011, p. 314].

Features	Accuracy
UNIGRAMS$_{\text{SVM}}$	88.4
BIGRAMS$_{\text{SVM}}$+	89.6
TRIGRAMS$_{\text{SVM}}$+	89.0
UNIGRAMS$_{\text{NB}}$	88.4
BIGRAMS$_{\text{NB}}$+	88.9

The Ott study also reports good accuracy in distinguishing true from false narratives using POS tag frequencies (73.0%) and LIWC features (76.8%), as well as LIWC+bigrams (89.8%) when testing with the SVM classifier, but the n-gram scores are particularly remarkable in light of the accuracy scores that M&S achieved with n-grams. What makes them so?

The main difference between the M&S experiment and the Ott experiment is in the highly constrained topic of hotel reviews covered by Ott as opposed to subjects' expressions of opinions on hot-button issues, which can be much more diverse. It is encouraging, though, that given the lack of diversity in the hotel reviews, at least in their lexicon, Ott et al. still finds a sharp difference between the truthful and the deceptive reviews. On the other hand, the true reviewers are prompted by TripAdvisor to rate the hotel on several parameters, including location, sleep quality, rooms, service, value, and cleanliness, and reviewers tend to repeat these words in their reviews. Ott does not report the bogus reviewers being given these prompts.

---

[8]TripAdvisor.com reviews are not backed up by transactional data; anyone can submit a review. To weed out bogus reviews, TripAdvisor employs a fraud detection team and has software that tracks the reviews for anomalies [Reiter, 2007].

Ott et al. [2011] studied only favorable reviews, both truthful and deceptive. But negative reviews—those assigned 1 or 2 stars by the reviewer—can be even more damaging to a brand than are favorable reviews for a competitor. **Ott-13** looks at reviews that bad-mouth the competition [Ott et al., 2013]. The design of the negative review study is almost identical to Ott's previous study—400 T reviews, 20 reviews per hotel, and 400 F reviews, 20 reviews per hotel—with F reviews written by Turkers. The T reviews, however, come from multiple sources for the negative study; in addition to TripAdvisor, these include Expedia, Hotels.com, Orbitz, Priceline, and Yelp. The average length of the negative reviews, at 178 words, is also substantially longer than the positive reviews, at 116 words.

To provide a baseline for this specific study, three undergraduate university students were asked to make T/F judgments on 40 T and 40 F reviews from each of four hotels. The use of human judges also ensured that the F reviews were convincing. While the best human judge had an accuracy rate of 65%, the interrater agreement among the judges was low (Fleiss kappa at 0.07; Cohen's kappa at 0.26 for the pairwise agreement between the two most accurate judges).

The automated classification for the negative review study was done in the same manner as for the positive reviews but only unigram and bigram features were tested. The expanded data set of 800 positive and 800 negative reviews allowed for three training situations: train using positive sentiment data only, train using negative only, and train using both positive and negative data. Table 4.6 gives the accuracy scores for each situation, showing that the combined situation gives the best overall results, possibly because of the larger training set, as the Ott-13 paper speculates.

Table 4.6: Measures (%) of Ott-13's SVM classifier on negative and positive reviews. "Held out" refers to classifiers trained on reviews of one sentiment and tested on the other. "Cross Val." refers to "5-fold stratified cross-validation" where the model is trained on reviews for 16 hotels and tested on reviews for the remaining hotels, with sentiment as indicated in the table.

Train Sentiment	Test Sentiment	Accuracy	True F-measure	False F-measure
POSITIVE (800 reviews)	POSITIVE (800 reviews, Cross Val.)	89.3	89.2	89.3
	NEGATIVE (800 reviews, Held Out)	75.1	78.6	70.3
NEGATIVE (800 reviews)	POSITIVE (800 reviews, Held Out)	81,4	83.0	79.4
	NEGATIVE (800 reviews, Cross Val.)	86.0	85.9	86.1
COMBINED (1600 reviews)	POSITIVE (800 reviews, Cross Val.)	88.4	88.5	88.3
	NEGATIVE (800 reviews, Cross Val.)	86.0	86.1	85.9

The results also show that training on one sentiment and testing on the other lowers accuracy, suggesting that "cues to deception differ depending on the sentiment of the text."

Ott-13 also looks at the language of the reviews, finding that F reviews, unlike T reviews, are scarce on spatial details and include more verbs relative to nouns, which, Ott suggests, parallel the characteristics of imaginative writing and recall the claims of Reality Monitoring (see Chapter 2). However, while first-person pronoun usage in the positive-only study occurred at twice the rate in F reviews as in T, it was only 57% higher in the F negative reviews. Not surprisingly, though, positive reviews express more positive emotions and negative reviews more negative ones, capturing, as Ott observes, the sentiment of the writers rather than the negativity associated with deception, as represented in DePaulo et al.'s [2003] Self-Presentational approach discussed in Chapter 2.

Hernández Fusilier et al. [2014] **(H-F)**, citing the difficulty of constructing large data sets like that of Ott-13 in real application scenarios, propose the semi-supervised PU-learning method to build a training set of positive and negative reviews from known positive (P), deceptive data and unlabeled (U) data [Hernández Fusilier et al., 2014]. The method is chosen because of prior success in dealing with data showing high cohesion, as does the target (positive) class of T reviews, and high variation in the unlabeled set due, we would assume, to the mixture of cohesive positive T reviews with more diverse positive F reviews as well as negative T and F reviews.

H-F tests the original PU-learning algorithm, which iteratively builds a training set of "reliable negative" data, against their modified PU-learning algorithm, which eliminates negative data of lesser reliability, yielding a smaller number of "high quality negative instances." Given this 3-way set of classes—positive/negative, T/F, and PU-original/PU-modified—H-F test (1) the feasibility of PU-learning for this realistic situation, (2) the superiority of the PU-modified algorithm, and (3) the effect of the positive/negative polarity under PU-learning. They also compare the performance of unigrams vs. uni+bigrams and Naïve Bayes vs. SVM classifiers.

These tests show that the PU-modified algorithm achieved a best F-measure of 0.7 in the classification of negative opinions using 120 labeled deceptive opinions for training and a best F-measure of 0.79 "in the detection of positive deceptive and truthful opinions using only 100 labeled training samples." H-F notes that the vocabulary of the negative opinions is larger than that for the positive "indicating their content is in general more detailed and diverse," requiring the larger training set. Overall, the PU-modified algorithm outperforms both a baseline measure using the whole unlabeled set as negatives for the training set as well as the PU-original algorithm, with an F-measure of 0.796 for both T and F positive opinions when trained on 100 positive F opinions and 520 unlabeled opinions. For both T and F negative opinions, the PU-modified algorithm achieves the same best F-measure as the PU-original algorithm, 0.699, when trained on 120 negative F opinions and 520 unlabeled opinions. Again, the lower F-measure and larger training set required demonstrates the greater difficulty of classifying negative opinions.

With respect to the use of a single polarity, positive or negative, to train as opposed to combining the two polarities into a larger training set, H-F's scores show that the combination results in superior performance. A combined training set of 240 F opinions and 1,040 unlabeled opinions achieves the top F-measure of 0.771 on F opinions and 0.790 on T opinions. This compares well to Ott-13's F-measures on combined polarity training sets (see Table 4.6), given that Ott-13's training data is all labeled.

Finally, H-F tested the performance of the PU-learning method on discrimination of positive vs. negative reviews using unigrams and uni+bigrams with Naïve Bayes and SVM classifiers. H-F found that PU-learning providing data to the NB classifier gives the best results on predicting positive reviews, with an F-measure on unigrams of 0.796 (training data of 100 deceptive negative and 520 unlabeled reviews) and an F-measure on uni+bigrams of 0.778 (training data of 120 deceptive negative and 520 unlabeled reviews). For the prediction of negative reviews, the NB classifier provided the best results, with an F-measure of 0.699 on unigrams and 0.727 on uni+bigrams (training data of 120 deceptive negative and 520 unlabeled reviews).

In summary, H-F provides confirmation of Ott-13's claim with respect to using combined polarity data that more data, regardless of polarity, is better, from which we can infer that positive and negative reviews have more in common with each other than do True and False reviews. Negative deceptive opinions are harder to detect than positive deceptive opinions. And, for applications that require large training sets, PU-learning, particularly the modified learning proposed by H-F, provides a reasonable means of generating a large training set from a small set of known positive deceptive opinions and a large set of unlabeled opinions.

Fornaciari and Poesio [2014] (**F&P-14**) advance the same goal as H-F: to build a data set for deception research by maximizing the estimate of ground truth for reviews whose T/F value is not known with a high degree of certainty [Fornaciari and Poesio, 2014]. Instead of the semi-supervised approach of H-F, however, the authors use what we might term sleuthing to discover the veracity of Amazon book reviews, working with Jeremy Duns, a writer who had unmasked a number of bogus Amazon book reviewers. F&P-14 establishes 118 reviews as false "with a high degree of confidence," based primarily on reviewer admission of their falsity[9] and 118 reviews as true based on the pointlessness of paying someone to write a False review of books by dead authors (Conan Doyle and Kipling are named) or best-selling living authors (Ken Follett and Stephen King are named). This is their gold-standard data. An additional 4,112 reviews are labeled as true and 2,471 are labeled False based on four cues to deception: (1) reviews identified in news articles as purchased; (2) reviews of a single book that all appear within a short period of time, suggesting that the reviews were purchased on deadline; (3) reviews by reviewers who did not use their real name;[10] and (4) lack of transactional data that the reviewer actually purchased the book from Amazon. This is their silver-standard data. The mean length of each review was 172.37 tokens—close to the length of the negative reviews of Ott-13.

F&P-14 do not discuss the overall content of the books reviewed; however, the one false review that is associated with a book is titled *Write Your First Book*, while the true reviews, whose content might be inferred based on the named authors, appear to be fiction. If non-fiction books feed the false reviews while fiction books feed the true categories, this would be a confounding

---

[9]We give a more detailed description of the F&P-14 data collection and verification work in Chapter 5, where we discuss ground truth annotation.
[10]Amazon enables reviewers to register using a pseudonym.

factor for F&P-14 since the vocabulary used to review a non-fiction book may be quite different from that used to review a work of fiction.

F&P-14 advance a second goal: to learn the best classifier jointly with the ground truth. For the classification experiments, F&P-14 use a fairly standard set of features for the review vectors, including the most frequent n-grams with the highest Information Gain (discriminatory power), their lemmas and parts of speech, and the length of the review. The silver-standard reviews comprise the training set; the gold-standard reviews, the test set.

F&P-14 test two methods of classification, Majority Voting and Learning from Crowds [Raykar et al., 2010]. Raykar's algorithm improves on Majority Voting by evaluating the skill of each voter (or "annotator") on True vs. False from past performance on already-seen annotation. The study's use of its deception cues distinguishes the two methods. Under Majority Voting, if a review has more than two of the four cues, it is classified as False, otherwise, True. Under Learning from Crowds, each cue[11] is treated as an annotator and weighted based on prior performance discriminating T from F on already seen reviews. Again, the cues are being used to establish the silver-standard ground truth, but with track being kept of their success at discriminating T from F.

F&P-14 achieve a total accuracy score of 75.42% on Majority Voting, and 76.27% on Learning from Crowds, with F-measures of 72.12% and 75.22%, respectively, which is comparable to H-Fs PU-learning results on T/F discrimination. Majority Voting does particularly well on Precision (83.33%), but at the sacrifice of Recall (63.56%). Learning from Crowds, on the other hand, has more balanced results: Precision: 78.70%; Recall: 72.03%.

Methods that build large training sets from product review data whose True/False status is not known a priori, such as those of H-F and F&P-14, are suitable for applications like the estimation of the likelihood of a product review being false. For most products purchased online, this estimate should be helpful enough. It is important to keep in mind, though, that some types of review—doctor recommendations, for example—are more critical and may require the higher level of confidence that only a gold standard can give. It is conceivable that, with enough effort, positive reviews could be obtained in these critical areas; it is harder to imagine obtaining much negative data but F&P-14 describe sleuthing techniques that might be cleverly adapted to this task.

4.3.2 FEATURES

The difficulty of validating narratives for ground truth results in the production of small datasets, making the use of statistical techniques on n-grams relatively ineffective unless the data is constrained in other ways, primarily by topic choice, as suggested in the previous section. As we have seen there, this constraint enables the use of semi-supervised learning to build larger datasets for applications like the Twitter scams of Chen et al. [2014] and hotel reviews of Hernández Fusilier et al. [2014], where the language is highly constrained.

---

[11]For reasons internal to the algorithm, F&P do not use the first cue.

Where the language is less constrained, however, most computational studies of deception have turned to some form of generalization over a set of *n*-grams, above and beyond stemming, to boost the amount of relevant data. The features METAPHYSICAL and OPTIMISM noted by M&S exemplify this technique and several of the computational deception studies have made use of the LIWC categories that M&S briefly compare to their *n*-gram approach, while others have made use of a variety of features to capture differences between truthful and deceptive language.

Studies Using Surface Features

Burgoon et al. [2003] is the earliest automated effort we know that discriminated true from false narratives. It reports the analysis of verbal data from a mock theft where half the participants are instructed to steal a wallet and lie about the theft and the other half not steal and tell the truth, yielding 49 interview narratives, 29 of which were conducted via text chat and 20 via audio chat.

Burgoon used features that are the least context sensitive and the most amenable to automation, including:

1. quantity (number of syllables, words, sentences);

2. vocabulary Complexity (number of big [*sic*] words, number of syllables per word);

3. grammatical Complexity (number of short sentences, number of long sentences, Flesh-Kincaid grade level, average number of words per sentence, sentence complexity, number of conjunctions); and

4. specificity and expressiveness (emotiveness index, rate of adjectives and adverbs, number of affective terms).

The features were obtained using a shallow parser ("Grok or Iskim") and dictionary look-up. Using a C4.5 decision tree algorithm [Quinlan, 1993] and 15-fold cross-validation, Burgoon et al. [2004] obtained an accuracy of 59.7% as represented in Table 4.7

Table 4.7: Confusion matrix produced by Burgoon et al.'s C4.5 tree

		Predicted Class	
		True	False
Actual Class	True	27	19
	False	10	16

Using Burgoon's baseline of human judgments, which are "typically very poor at detecting deception and fallacious information, their "prediction rate" of 60.72%[12] is significant and supported the use of linguistic features to separate truthful from deceptive language.

[12]We are assuming that the 1% discrepancy between Burgoon et al.'s accuracy score as derived from Table 4.7 and their quoted "prediction rate" results from a difference between the two measures that is not explicitly stated in the article.

Zhou et al. [2004b] tests 19 cues motivated by various theories of deception. Zhou et al. [2004a] describes the cues, the NLP techniques used to implement each cue, and the significance level of each cue with respect to its discriminatory power. Zhou et al. [2004b] are able to achieve a remarkable level of discrimination on laboratory-generated email exchanges of student pairs working on a modified version of the Desert Survival Problem [Lafferty et al., 1974] in which the subjects were to achieve a consensus ranking of 12 items necessary for survival after a jeep crash in the Kuwaiti desert. In two slightly different experiments a total of 112 subjects exchanged a maximum of 3 emails per subject with a total of 29 email senders instructed to deceive in their arguments for their preferred ranking.

The main goal of Zhou et al. [2004b] is to compare the performance of four statistical methods—discriminant analysis, logistic regression, decision trees, and neural networks—in discriminating T from F narratives. The study provides a rationale for the varying performance of each method on (1) the collection of individual messages (the "message data") and (2) the "estimate of each cue in individual messages . . . averaged by subject" (the "subject data"). The study also considers the performance of the four methods on the full set of 19 cues compared to the performance on only the most discriminatory cues with the latter yielding better accuracy scores across all four.

Zhou et al. [2004b] achieve a high degree of accuracy—as much as 88.5% with the neural network on the subject data and 74.5% on the message data—using the highly discriminatory cues. This is particularly remarkable given that the study is among the earliest deception detection implementations. The data generated by the Desert Survival task, is, like the hotel review data, highly constrained, making the cue identification more tractable, but the discrimination task is still difficult, which makes the specific cues and the neural networks both look like promising contributors to the high performance. The study is careful to separate out the possible differences given genre and medium of communication.

The one drawback of Zhou et al. [2004b] is the laboratory setting in which deceivers are instructed to lie, with no threat and, indeed, support for their fabrications. This raises the issue of ecological validity and the related issue, considered in Ott et al. [2011], as to the relation between deceptive and imaginative narrative. We will return to this issue in Chapter 5.

Bachenko et al. [2008] (**BFS**) was the first computational deception study to use real-world data taken from multiple sources, including three criminal statements, two police interrogations, a tobacco lawsuit deposition, and Jeffrey Skilling's congressional testimony on the Enron failure. It established the veracity of individual propositions using police reports, court testimony, meeting minutes, videotapes, etc. as well as contradictions in the narrative such as a confession at its end. From these corroborations, it was able to assign T/F values to 275 propositions in its 25,687 words of narrative, 164 False and the remainder True.

BFS used 12 linguistic features cited in the psychology and criminal justice literature that can be formally represented and automated in an NLP system. The features are of three types: [13]

1. lack of commitment in which the narrator uses linguistic means to avoid making a direct statement. These features include hedges, qualified assertions in which it remains unclear whether an action was performed (e.g., *I needed to get my inhaler*), unexplained lapses of time (*later that day*), overzealous expressions (*I swear to God*), and rationalizations (*I was unfamiliar with the road*);

2. negativity. These features include negative forms (*never, inconceivable*), negative emotions (*I was a nervous wreck*), and memory loss (*I forget*); and

3. inconsistencies in verb and noun forms including verb tense changes, thematic role changes (e.g., a NP shifting from agent to patient), different NP forms for the same referent (*my family* becomes *some people*) and changes in pronoun usage.

BFS hypothesize that the density distribution of these features correlates with deception. To instantiate this they use a moving average to score each word in a narrative, with each indicator and proximity to an indicator lowering the average. The moving average enables the automatic segmentation of the narrative into non-overlapping regions that are identified as likely true, likely deceptive or somewhere in between.

Converting the likely true and likely deceptive segments into T and F, respectively, BFS achieve the results represented in Table 4.8 with an accuracy of 74.9%.

Table 4.8: T/F classification based on BFS's cue density algorithm

		Predicted Class		
		True	False	Accuracy (%)
Actual Class	True	124	40	75.6
	False	29	82	73.8

BFS also point out that by raising the cut-off score for False, the system can favor high recall or high precision for T or F as the application requires; for example, in cases where investigators are looking for leads, high recall could be valuable in and of itself at the expense of high precision.

The accuracy of the BFS result is substantial given the diversity of the data and the real world language and source checking. It is also worth noting here the observation by both DePaulo et al. [2003] and Vrij [2008] that the next step forward in deception research would be in the identification of clusters of cues. Computational methods enable the recognition of clusters, and the scoring and moving average technique of BFS is the first algorithm, as far as we know, that identifies clusters of deception cues.

[13]Several of these features are not purely surface features; qualified assertions, thematic role changes, and referent checking require parse tree information, while rationalizations require human judgment.

Studies that Lack CL Properties but with Interesting Observations

While they do not propose a predictive model for deception, Keila and Skillicorn [2005] point to an interesting application of automatic deception detection: the ranking of a large set of documents, in this case the 494,833 emails of the Enron dataset, to reflect "their importance for discovering malfeasance inside an organization" [Keila and Skillicorn, 2005].

Zhou et al. [2004a] laid the groundwork for Zhou et al. [2004b] by evaluating 27 verbal cues identified as "amenable to automation." The study looked for significant differences in the occurrence of these cues in truthful vs. deceptive messages, which were, as mentioned above, laboratory-generated emails involving the Desert Survival Problem. The study provides sometimes tractable ways of measuring abstract theoretical claims against truthful and deceptive emails. Uncertainty, for example, is measured by the occurrence of modifiers, modal verbs, third person pronouns, as well as words that directly indicate uncertainty such as *maybe*. While the study does not provide a predictive model of deception, it connects several of the more abstract cues from the literature to concrete, linguistically based measures.

The Lexical Inquiry and Word Count Features

The LIWC features grew out of attempts by the psychologists James Pennebaker and Martha Francis [Pennebaker and Francis, 1996, Pennebaker et al., 1997] to predict cognitive change by counting relevant words in a narrative, with cognitive change defined as the use of words in two general text dimensions: self-reflective thinking and causal thinking. The self-reflection category includes words such as *realize, understand, think,* and *consider.* The causal thinking category includes words such as *cause, effect, reason,* and *because,* [Pennebaker et al., 1997, p. 864]. In addition to the 32 word categories capturing psychological constructs, the current LIWC application includes 4 general descriptor categories (total word count, words per sentence, percentage of words captured by the dictionary, and percentage of words longer than 6 letters), 22 standard linguistic dimensions (e.g., percentage of words in the text that are pronouns, articles, auxiliary verbs, etc.), 7 personal concern categories (e.g., work, home, leisure activities), 3 paralinguistic dimensions (assents, fillers, nonfluencies), and 12 punctuation categories (periods, commas, etc.) [Pennebaker et al., 2007, p. 4]. The words classified within the psychological categories were based on word lists from common emotion rating scales, *Roget's Thesaurus,* English dictionaries, and input by human judges at various stages of development. As far as we know, word membership in the categories has not been empirically tested against psychological processes like adaptive bereavement, for which the LIWC predecessor was originally designed, to determine the goodness of fit of each word in the category.

The computational use of the LIWC categories to distinguish true from false narratives began with an advisee of James Pennebaker, Matthew Newman, a Ph.D. candidate in psychology at the University of Texas-Austin at the time. Newman's study analyzed the language used by student subjects giving both a false account and a true account of their feelings on the topics of abortion and friends [Newman et al., 2003]. On the topic of abortion, subjects were either asked to speak their true and false opinions, to type them, or to handwrite them, Subjects also participated in a mock crime in which half were told to steal a dollar bill and all were told to deny taking the money. This resulted in five studies with no subjects in common. As a baseline, Newman used a panel of 7–9 human judges who evaluated the abortion narrators as reporting their true feelings or not.

The unique characteristic of the Newman work is that it used the LIWC features to categorize language as deceptive or true. To test the ability of the features to predict T vs. F, Newman selected the five features that were most discriminatory and entered them into a logistic regression to test the ability of the feature distribution cross-topic, training on four of the studies and testing on the fifth. The selected highly discriminatory features of deception were: fewer first-person singular pronouns, fewer third-person pronouns, more negative emotion words, fewer exclusive words, and more motion verbs.

Newman reports an overall accuracy on the five studies of 61%, which differs significantly from the judges accuracy of 52%. While the overall accuracy is suggestive of the ability of the LIWC categories to distinguish T from F narratives, the dependence of the accuracy score on topic is notable, with the abortion narratives inter alia producing the higher scores while the overall accuracy of the four stories to predict the friends narrative was 53% and to predict the mock crime was 48%, much lower than M&S's cross-topic accuracy on their simple n-gram study represented in Table 4.3.

Also notable is the fact that only one linguistic dimension, references to self, was a discriminatory feature in both the Newman et al. and the M&S post hoc study, despite the fact that two of the three topics in both studies were abortion and friends.

We have already considered the results of Ott et al. [2011] with respect to n-grams, but the study considers three perspectives on the detection of deception with respect to their online hotel review data, regarding it not only as (1) a text classification task, but also as (2) a case of psycholinguistic deception detection, in which we expect deceptive statements to exemplify the psychological effects of lying, such as increased negative emotion and psychological distancing; and as (3) a case of genre identification in which the deceptive statements are seen as cases of imaginative writing while the truthful statements are seen as cases of informative writing.

The results of the Ott et al. [2011] classification task showed accuracy scores as high as 89.6% for bigrams using a SVM classifier. The results of the psychological approach, which the study implements with the LIWC features, does not perform well by comparison, scoring 76.8%, although use of the LIWC features does boost the bigram/SVM performance to 89.8%.

Ott et al. [2011] also consider deceptive and truthful writing as subgenres of imaginative and informative writing respectively, citing the work of Johnson and Raye [1981] on Reality Monitoring and following up on linguistic work by Rayson et al. [2001], which argued that imaginative writing consists of more verbs, adverbs, pronouns, and pre-determiners while informative writing consists of more nouns, adjectives, prepositions, determiners, and coordinating conjunctions. Using these patterns, Ott et al. argues for the promise of viewing T/F discrimination as a genre identification task, with POS distribution capturing genre representation. The POS /SVM classifier was able to discriminate their T/F hotel reviews with an accuracy of 73%,

In many laboratory experiments, it is unclear whether the subjects are truly deceiving or, because of the lack of threat and the sanctioning of the lying, they are merely being inventive. If a robust link between deceptive and imaginative narration could be supported, it would go a long way toward supporting the use of laboratory data in deception studies, an issue that we consider in more detail in Chapter 5.

Larcker and Zakolyukina [2010] (**L&Z**) tested LIWC categories on real world data: the financial health of companies as represented in quarterly earnings conference calls, which we discussed in Chapter 3. L&Z selected LIWC categories that they believed to be particularly relevant to their topic and added financial vocabulary to the LIWC categories.

The L&Z narrative data consists of the Q&A portions of quarterly earnings conference calls. It contains 16,577 CEO narratives and 14,462 CFO narratives, with a "narrative" being the turn taken in answer to a question on a call. The ground truth data comes from subsequent financial restatements identified by Glass Lewis & Co., with conference call narratives labeled as deceptive "if they involve substantial subsequent restatement of net income and are associated with more severe types of restatements" [Larcker and Zakolyukina, 2010, pp. 2-3]. This resulted in 10% of the narratives being labeled as "deceptive" and a greater weight put on deceptive narratives in the analysis to balance out these "rare" events.

A greater difficulty than the imbalance, however, is the fact that "some manipulated quarters are never restated or restated outside of the time period we examine" (fn. 14), which means that some transcripts labeled as true may actually be deceptive. Still, L&Z demonstrate that the language of the deceptive transcripts is distinctive, with accuracy rates as high as 65% for CEOs and 58% for CFOs. Another issue with the use of restatements is the question of whether the call participants actually know about a manipulation at the time of the call. In imposing the higher bar on the types and levels of restatement that are used for their ground truth annotation, L&Z's aim is to ensure that the original fraud would have been so severe that it would be difficult to imagine the participants not knowing about it.

The time-sensitivity of the T/F determination is peculiar to financial data, where a narrative can flip from T to F several years later. It is less likely to arise in the studies that use legal data, where true statements can be established on the basis of investigation, although legal data is not immune from subsequent discovery of new facts.

Fornaciari and Poesio [2011] (**F&P**) test various permutations of the LIWC categories as well as "surface features" on the real-world utterances from their Italian DeCour (Deception in Courts) corpus of criminal proceedings from three court jurisdictions in Italy where the defendant was found guilty of false testimony.

F&P use 623 utterances from 10 hearings as a training set and test on 148 utterances from 4 different hearings. The T/F status of these utterances was clearly identified. F&P use "surface feature vectors" that include lemmas and parts of speech as well as bigrams and trigrams of these

Table 4.9: Performance of F&P's surface features on their DeCour data

	Correctly classified	Incorrectly classified	Precision	Recall	F-measure
False	35	32	0.729	0.522	0.609
True	68	13	0.680	0.840	0.751
Total	103	45			

Table 4.10: LIWC categories' performance on F&P's DeCour data

	Correctly classified	Incorrectly classified	Precision	Recall	F-measure
False	33	34	0.868	0.493	0.629
True	76	5	0.691	0.938	0.796
Total	109	39			

as a baseline against which to compare the more abstract LIWC features. The results of these surface features, shown in Table 4.9, reinforce the findings of M&S that significant distinctions can be found between the language of truth and of lies even at the level of the *n*-gram, and, for F&P, even on linguistically quite diverse real-world data.

For purposes of comparison, the accuracy rate here is 69.5%, which is remarkable given the data; the false testimony data resulted from lies told at the original trials, which covered an enormous range of data from fraudulent claims of lost checks to drug trafficking to homicide.

To test whether some form of the LIWC features could perform better, F&P built five kinds of vectors, using the Italian LIWC dictionary [Agosti and Rellini, 2007]: (1) all 29 of the categories used by Newman, (2) all 85 features of the Italian LIWC dictionary plus the general descriptor categories, (3) the 29 most discriminatory features from the second vector, (4) Newman's 5 most discriminatory categories, and (5) the 5 most discriminatory features from the second vector.

Table 4.10 shows the results of Newman's 29 categories, the best performing of the vectors, on the DeCour data. For purposes of comparison, the accuracy score here is 73.6%, only slightly better than the 69.5% of the surface feature model.

With the use of precision and recall, F&P call attention to the usefulness of a system with even moderate accuracy. All five vectors have recall rates of True utterances above 90%, with F&P's own five vectors recalling Trues at a remarkable 98.8%. While none of the vectors have high recall of false utterances, the "Newman 29" vector has fairly high precision (86.8%) in predicting False. If an application needed to be sure to identify all the true utterances and/or be sure that the utterances identified as False were clearly false, these vectors would serve the purpose.

Table 4.11: F-measure performance of LIWC by category from Almela et al.

LIWC Category	Homosexual Adoption	Bullfighting	Best Friend	Total
1. linguistic	0.638	0.679	0.763	0.683
2. psychologic	0.678	0.624	0.780	0.702
3. descriptors	0.620	0.620	0.695	0.616
4. personal	0.506	0.525	0.639	0.561

Table 4.12: F-measure performance of LIWC by category combinations from Almela et al.

LIWC Categories	Homosexual Adoption	Bullfighting	Best Friend	Total
1 & 2	0.709	0.655	0.83	0.736
1, 2, 3, 4	0.718	0.660	0.845	0.734
2 & 3	0.724	0.619	0.81	0.723

Almela et al. [2012], using a version of LIWC2001 [Ramirez-Esparza et al., 2007] that "has been fully validated for Spanish across several psycholinguistic studies," classify a data set similar to that of Mihalcea and Strapparava, trained and tested using each category of LIWC (psychological constructs, general descriptors, standard linguistic dimensions, and personal concerns) separately and then in the possible combinations of the four categories. The results for the singleton categories by topic and cross-topic are shown in Table 4.11; the scores represent F-measure.

The best performing combinations of LIWC categories are shown in Table 4.12. Again, the scores represent F-measures.

Almela's top score across all LIWC tests and topics is 84.5% using the combination of all four categories on the Best Friend topic. For comparison with the other LIWC studies that cite F-measure, Ott et al.'s highest F-measure is 76.9% using the LIWC features alone on the more lexically constrained hotel reviews and Fornaciari and Poesio's is 79.6%

Almela et al. argue that the higher performance, in general, on the Best Friend topic shows the strong dependence of the task on topic and hypothesize that the better performance on this topic may be due to the greater emotional involvement that narrators have in describing their best friend. There may also be a better alignment between the LIWC vocabulary and the Best Friend topic than between LIWC and the other topics.

For the purposes of categorizing deceptive narrative, then, it would seem more productive to determine which words are more highly discriminatory and then to determine whether category generalizations can be made across these words.

4.3.3   STUDIES LOOKING ABOVE THE LEXICAL LEVEL

In addition to the words and phrases that might distinguish true from false narratives, the background literature has found some discriminative power in other levels of language analysis. According to DePaulo et al. [2003], at the acoustic and prosodic level, for example, statistically significant differences have been found in vocal tension [Horvath, 1978, 1979] and higher pitch [Zuckerman et al., 1979]. At the syntactic level, statistically significant differences have been found in longer, more detailed sentences [Porter and Yuille, 1996]. At the semantic level, plausibility, narrative consistency and coherence [Köhnken et al., 1995, Porter and Yuille, 1996, Sporer, 1997, Zaparniuk et al., 1995], as well as internal consistency [DePaulo et al., 1982], [Heinrich and Borkenau, 1998], and [Zuckerman et al., 1982] have been found to show statistically significant differences between true and false narratives. And at the level of discourse, the length of the prologue partition [Adams, 2002, Adams and Jarvis, 2006] has been shown to be differentiating.

Studies have only begun to explore the ability of these other levels of analysis to discriminate true from false narratives. We cover here the research known to us.

Among the laboratory data studies, Hirschberg et al. [2005] comes the closest to satisfying ecological validity in a scenario similar to that of Ekman and Friesen's 1974 Nurses Study. Thirty-two MBA students were asked to perform tasks in six areas where their performance, they were told, would be compared to twenty-five "top entrepreneurs of America." The subjects were then asked to attempt to convince an interviewer that they had performed like the entrepreneurs, although the difficulty of the tasks had been manipulated so that only two scores appeared to be similar to the entrepreneurial performance, while two others were higher and two were lower. Thus, they would be giving two true accounts and four false ones. The subjects were also asked to press foot levers for each of their accounts to record whether each was true or false, as an added measure of ground truth.

While the Hirschberg study tested 68 LIWC categories, they also tested acoustic and prosodic features thought to be associated with deception, as well as speaker-dependent features, which included ratios of filled pauses in lying and truthful conditions for a given speaker as well as ratios of laughter and cue phrase use, and filled pauses to all phrases. The LIWC features reduced the error rate from a baseline 39.8% to 39%; the acoustic and prosodic features reduced it to 38.5%, but the most impressive reduction comes from the combined LIWC, acoustic-prosodic, and speaker-dependent features, which reduced the error rate to 33.6%, lending support to the notion that the truthful and lying behavior is, at least partially, speaker dependent. Recall here the polygraph procedure, which establishes a baseline for each interviewee with mutually known ground truth questions before serious questioning begins.

Feng et al. [2012a] (**FBC**) add Probabilistic Context Free Grammar production rules [Petrov and Klein, 2007] to the n-gram model tested by Mihalcea and Strapparava (2009) and to the n-gram + part-of-speech model of Ott et al. (2011).

FBC test four different levels of PCFG production rules:

Table 4.13: Top accuracy scores (%) for Ott (2011), M&S (2011), and FBC (2012) models. Numbers in parentheses are from FBC's implementation of M&S; M&S do not test a bigram model. Numbers in italics are results reported by Ott et al. [2011] and Mihalcea and Strapparava [2009].

		TripAdvisor	Abortion	Best Friend	Death Penalty
words	unigram	*88.4*	*70.0*	*77.0*	*67.4*
	bigram	*89.6*	(71.5)	(70.5)	(55.5)
PCFG + unigram	$\hat{r}$ + *unigram*	88.5	**77.0**	81.5	70.5
	$\hat{r} * + unigram$	90.3	74.0	**85.0**	**71.5**
	$\hat{r} * + unigram$	**91.2**	76.0	84.5	71.0

- r: unlexicalized production rules (i.e., all production rules except for those with terminal nodes) e.g., $NP_2 \rightarrow NP_3$ SBAR;

- $r*$: lexicalized production rules (i.e., all production rules), including those with terminal nodes, e.g., $PRP \rightarrow$ "you";

- $\hat{r}$: unlexicalized production rules combined with the grandparent node, e.g., $NP2\hat{\ }VP1 \rightarrow NP3$ SBAR; and

- $\hat{r}*$: lexicalized production rules (i.e., all production rules) combined with the grandparent node, e.g., $PRP\hat{\ }NP4 \rightarrow$ "you" .

They demonstrate that the PCFG rules provide a substantial gain over these approaches, as Table 4.13 showing best performances in boldface, demonstrates. Most impressive is the fact that the gain is achieved not only on product review data (FBC test on YELP restaurant reviews as well as on Ott et al.'s hotel reviews) but also on M&S's essay data, which includes the widely divergent topics of abortion, the death penalty, and best friends.

FBC also test a second set of TripAdvisor hotel data, with 400 truthful and 400 deceptive reviews based on spam detection heuristics introduced in Feng et al. [2012b], i.e., both the True and False reviews in the Heuristic data set occurred "in the wild" as opposed to the gold-standard data, which involved Mechanical Turkers writing the False reviews. It is worth noting that the various models perform more poorly on this "TripAdvisor-Heuristic" data than on Ott's gold-standard data (see Table 4.14), which suggests a revisiting of the question of how to obtain a gold-standard data set for deception.

Feng and Hirst [2013] (**F&H**) add to FBC's PCFG + unigram model a "collective profile" for each hotel in the Ott dataset, the collective profile being essentially a model of a true review for each hotel. The basic idea is that reviews by customers who have experienced the hotel will share common features of the experience that will be lacking—or even contradicted by—statements in

Table 4.14: Accuracy (%) results from two sets of TripAdvisor data. Numbers in italics are results reported by Ott et al. [2011].

		TripAdvisor	
		Gold	Heuristic
words	unigram	*88.4*	**74.4**
	bigram	*89.6*	71.5
PCFG + unigram	$\hat{r} + unigram$	88.5	74.3
	$r * + unigram$	90.3	75.4
	$\hat{r} * + unigram$	**91.2**	**76.6**

deceptive reviews. (Recall the cohesive property of true reviews cited by Hernández Fusilier et al. [2014].) The profile consists of distinct aspects usually realized as proper noun phrases that refer to landmarks near the hotel and general aspects, for example, for hotels: location, service, and breakfast. The descriptors of these aspects are pulled from the narratives and assigned a weight. For distinct aspects, the weight is based on the frequency of the aspect in the review collection; for general aspects, the weight is assigned to the descriptor words describing the aspect. In the example given by F&H, "Michigan Ave," a distinct aspect, is assigned a weight of 5.0, while the general aspect "Room" has descriptors "wonderful" with a weight of 4.0, "deluxe," 2.0, and "huge," 2.0.

A profile is also built for each review to be judged as T or F and each of these test profiles is compared—"aligned"—to the collective profile and vice versa. When the test profile is aligned to the collective profile, the representativeness of the test profile as a case of the collective profile is tested; when the collective profile is aligned with the test profile, any conflicts in the test profile are caught.

This alignment yields a list of compatibility features for each test profile that enable measurement of the distance between the test profile and the collective profile, the more distant, the more deceptive.

F&H reimplement the Ott and FBC models in order to add their profile alignment compatibility model to combinations of Ott's *n*-gram and FBC's syntactic (*SYN*) models. Testing on these reimplemented baseline models yields the accuracy scores in Table 4.15.

F&H add their profile alignment model to these results to achieve an accuracy of **91.3%**, "significantly better . . . than the baseline in Table 4.15, using the Wilcoxon sign-rank test (p<.05)."

The chief question for the profile approach is whether it can be generalized to domains other than hotel reviews. F&H believe it should work on other product reviews, "as long as the aspects are realized by noun phrases, especially that distinct aspects are realized by proper noun phrases." Extending this approach beyond product reviews may go beyond F&H's intent, but it

Table 4.15: Results for Feng and Hirst's reimplementation of the Ott and FBC models

Features	Baseline Accuracy
SYN	87.9
n-GRAM	89.6
1-GRAM + SYN	88.9
2-GRAM + SYN	89.0
N-GRAM + SYN	90.1

is worth noting that F&H do similarity matching only on exact words. The small lexical range of hotel reviews allows for success with this approach but one can imagine similarity measures that allow for the wider lexical range of more diverse domains.

Rubin and Vashchilko [2012] (**R&V**) do not provide an overall evaluation measure, but their study does provide a new level of analysis that is worth exploring: the discourse structure of the narrative. This approach is supported by the criminal justice research discussed in Chapter 2, Section 2.4, including Criteria-based Content Analysis [Steller and Köhnken, 1989, Undeutsch, 1989], Reality Monitoring [Köhnken et al., 1995], and Verbal Immediacy [Wiener and Mehrabian, 1968], all of whom have examined the discourse as a whole. Additionally, structural analysis that examines the length of the prologue, the event of interest, and the epilogue of written criminal statements [Adams, 2002, Adams and Jarvis, 2006] has yielded some results.

R&V operationalize this approach using Rhetorical Structure Theory [Mann and Thompson, 1988] in which a story is broken down into a hierarchical structure with the nodes indicating discourse relations—condition, concession, evidence, restatement, etc.—which describe how one part of a narrative connects to the other parts. Using these relations, their position in the narrative, and their co-occurrence with other relations for each narrative, R&V construct a vector space model for deceptive and for truthful narratives that enables them to classify the relations in 18 truthful and 18 deceptive stories, self-ranked as such by their Mechanical Turk authors on a seven-point Likert scale.

While lacking an evaluation measure, R&V do report the RST relations that significantly separate the truthful from the deceptive narratives, which account for "about one third of all RST relations based on difference in means test," including those shown in Table 16. Note the relation with the highest t score among the truthful stories, Evidence—not a surprising result but one that suggests R&V's approach is worth pursuing.

Finally, Santos and Li [2010] (**S&L**) propose argument formation as a differentiator of T and F narratives. While it analyzes only "simulated data based on an artificial story," the basic approach is worth further exploration. The premise of this work is that the "act of deceiving is composed of deceptive argument formation and argument communication," and that, while most work has concentrated on the cues found in the communication, deception is formed in the

Table 4.16: Comparison of normalized frequencies of RST relations in T and F stories: difference in means test

RST relationships appearing in the truthful stories with statistically significantly **GREATER** normalized frequencies than deceptive ones	RST relationships appearing in the truthful stories with statistically significantly **LOWER** normalized frequencies than deceptive ones
Antithesis (t=2.3299)	Preparation (t=-1.7533)
Evidence (t=3.7996)	Evaluation (t=-2.0762)
Joint (t=1.5961)	Disjunction (t=-1.7850)
Volitional cause (t=1.8597)	
Volitional result (t=1.8960)	

reasoning process that links arguments with evidence, making the reasoning process an object worthy of investigation and characterization.

S&L assumes a multiagent scenario in which the opinions that lead each agent to a decision are compared to those of the other agents in the scenario. A decision-making process involves facts (a knowledge base) and reasoning (an inference engine). A given agent is considered a deceiver if an agent's actual opinion on a given problem is very different [>4 standard deviations] from the predicted one, with the prediction based on calculations that feed a Bayesian Network.

As a testbed combining knowledge base and inferencing engine, S&L choose the Alarm Network [Beinlich et al., 1989], a decision system designed to monitor intensive care patients. To simulate differing opinions among multiple agents, S&L make small changes in the conditional probabilities of the network to yield the opinions of ten agents. The agents are then fed the same set of evidence, which initiates the inferencing. This process is repeated many times to obtain a set of historical opinions, which represent the behavior of the ten agents, with inferencing and opinions representing "normal decision error." This constitutes S&L's training data.

In testing for deception, S&L "rotate" each agent's posterior probabilities and measure the distance between the agent's predicted probabilities and these potentially deceptive ones, with a distance of 4 standard deviations or more interpreted as indicating deception. S&L tests the system on four different networks, producing a range of "correct" identifications of deception, represented by mean positive detection rates of: Alarm (88.84%), Hailfinder (80.92%), Diabetes (42.57%), and Munin (61.80%).

This approach should be promising given that deceivers "reach arguments from conclusions, while others reach conclusions from arguments" [Li and Santos, 2012]. However, while the knowledge bases and conditional probabilities are based on real-life decision support systems, the posterior probabilities are all simulated, leaving one to question whether the simulated behavior imitates real-life deceptive behavior. Another question involves the generalizability of the approach. Most scenarios that offer opportunities to deceive do not have scripts as rigid as the knowledge bases tested by S&L.

4.4   CONCLUSION

Mihalcea and Strapparava [2009] clearly demonstrated that *n*-gram distinctions alone are significantly better at distinguishing true from false narratives than the initial baseline of human performance on this task, while Ott et al. [2011] demonstrated that severely constraining the domain of the narratives can improve the differentiation remarkably.

With respect to the use of lexical features to capture generalizations about deceptive verbal behavior, we see mixed results, with the selected LIWC features of Newman et al. [2003], Larcker and Zakolyukina [2010], and Fornaciari and Poesio [2011] performing in the same range as Mihalcea and Strapparava's *n*-gram model. However, we have seen that it is difficult to compare these three studies given the distinctions between laboratory (Newman) and real-world (Larcker and Zakolyukina; Fornaciari and Poesio) data sources on the one hand and wide range of topic (Newman; Fornaciari and Poesio) on the other. The importance of topic range is further emphasized in Almela et al. [2012], also based on LIWC, which found the full set of LIWC features to function reasonably well on a topic (best friend) that seems well suited to the domains that LIWC was originally designed to cover while performing significantly less accurately on the other topics.

Feature sets other than those based on LIWC, including those used by Zhou et al. [2004b] and Bachenko et al. [2008] perform marginally better than LIWC on distinguishing true from false narratives, with Zhou's study emphasizing the importance of the choice of statistical method and Bachenko's the advantage of cue clustering and demonstration of the possibility of handling differing types of real-world data.

As the work on hotel reviews shows, narrowing the topic of the data set yields significant gains. The most recent work in this area, that of Feng and Hirst, which has built on prior work by Ott and Feng, Banerjee and Choi, results in an accuracy score of 91.3%, an accuracy high enough to be deployable, given the commercial application for which it is intended.

CHAPTER 5

Open Questions

5.1 INTRODUCTION

So, how far have we gotten, where are we now, and where do we go from here? Mihalcea and Strapparava [2009] clearly established that a NLP approach to separating truthful from deceptive narratives gives better results than a naïve human judge. And the basic n-gram technique on constrained language has yielded impressive results as demonstrated by Ott et al. [2011] with further enhanced NLP techniques, using that study's data, showing small but significant increments in performance.

One way to go is to expand out from the highly constrained language of hotel reviews to language domains with ever fewer constraints. To do this, some measure of "constrained" is necessary. To get such a measure, we need to consider contextual factors that the literature to date has only touched on. If expanding, we also need to revisit issues of ground truth annotation for real-world data given the large differences among product reviews, financial reports, legal testimony, and other areas where credibility needs to be assessed. And at some point here, the advantages of a common, shared data set will become apparent.

Finally, the question of cue clustering and the possibilities inherent in correlating verbal with non-verbal indicators of deception are areas that may yield new, valuable insights into identifying deceptive behavior.

5.2 IMPACT OF CONTEXTUAL FACTORS ON DECEPTIVE NARRATIVE

Burgoon notes that "It is likely that different cue models will be required for different tasks" [Burgoon et al., 2003, p. 6]. While Burgoon couched this observation in terms of deceiver adaptation to the task, it can be regarded more generally as anticipating the effect of factors like informative vs. imaginative genre on deceptive behavior.

How much do genre, topic, venue, register, and medium affect performance? We have looked at the consideration of genre in Ott et al.'s original study [Ott et al., 2011] and in Ott et al.'s positive/negative review study [Ott et al., 2013] where the language of the sentiment being expressed trumped the True/False classification. We have also touched on the difference that narrowing of topic makes in discussing the comparative accuracy of discriminating true from false hotel reviews as opposed to personal opinion narratives. How much difference does the choice of venue make? As the work of DePaulo et al. [2003] shows, there are significant differences between truthful and deceptive behavior in unplanned narratives that do not show up in planned narratives like political speeches. And, for systems that use features above the n-gram, are there correlations between the effectiveness of some features in discriminating deception and these contextual factors?

5.3 DECEPTIVE LANGUAGE AND IMAGINATIVE LANGUAGE

Ott et al. [2011], following work by Rayson et al. [2001], who used POS information to distinguish informative from imaginative language, use POS to distinguish truthful from deceptive language and find a distribution similar to Rayson et al., with truthful/informative language characterized by "more nouns, adjectives, prepositions, determiners, and coordinating conjunctions," while imaginative writing is characterized by "more verbs, adverbs, pronouns, and pre-determiners"[1] [Ott et al., 2011, p. 315].

The relation between deceptive and imaginative language is an important issue, since, as Chapter 3 discusses, many laboratory studies of deception involve subjects describing an event that they have not experienced. This, of course, is what fiction writers do, but with the foreknowledge of their readers that this is fiction. Careful laboratory studies try to distinguish the "deceptive" performance of their subjects from fictional narration by depriving the recipients of the narratives of this foreknowledge, i.e., the interviewers do not know which narratives are fact and which are fiction. Does the recipient's awareness of the fiction make a difference to the story teller's narrative?

Factors besides foreknowledge of the recipient play a role in deception. Fear, guilt and shame are involved in deception, at least in high-stakes deception, but not in imaginative story telling. The cognitive load in deception should also be greater than in imaginative story telling since the story teller only has to keep one story line straight while the liar has to keep the true events separate from the story s/he is telling. The purported negativity of the liar as opposed to the positive attitude of a storyteller may play into this distinction as well.

Clearly, there is room for more work like that of Ott et al. [2011] that will contribute to our knowledge of the similarities and differences between imaginative and deceptive language.

5.4 MEASURING THE DISTANCE BETWEEN DIVERSE NARRATIVES

Directly related to both the question of imaginative/deceptive narration and the contextual factors in which deception operates is the issue of how to measure the differences that each factor effects on the narrative. This is an issue of practical import since it should improve our success rates in moving out from highly constrained language to language domains with ever fewer constraints if we know how far we are moving.

---

[1]Past participles of verbs and superlative adverbs were exceptions.

What sorts of similarity measure are needed to estimate, for example, how good a hotel review model will be in discriminating true from bogus restaurant reviews? Service reviews? General product reviews?

Ott et al. [2011] reference Biber et al. [1999] and Rayson et al. [2001], which provide measures of genre similarity based on syntactic features. A seminal paper by Resnik provides a similarity measure based on concept similarity among the nodes of Word-Net's taxonomy [Resnik, 1995] and another foundational paper by Lin provides a notion of similarity based on a set of universal information-theoretic assumptions that is independent of any particular level of analysis [Lin, 1998]. Can any of these approaches, or the work that has followed from them, offer a distance measure between domains that would provide a prediction of the difficulty of accurately determining deceit in Domain B given an accurate measure of deceit for Domain A?

5.5 GROUND TRUTH ANNOTATION: THE SEARCH FOR GOLD-STANDARD DATA

Chapter 3 covers the sources and risks in assembling ground truth verification of real-world narratives, but how do we evaluate the truth-value of a particular claim or narrative? Gokhman et al. [2012] and Fitzpatrick and Bachenko [2012] begin a much-needed discussion on this issue for varying types of real-world data. Gokhman et al. discuss prior techniques for collecting deceptive and true data and consider in detail Ott's method of crowdsourcing to obtain deceptive content, which is offered as a gold standard for deceptive product reviews.

Ott's False reviews are known to be false; they have been purchased from Amazon Turkers, which seems to be a standard method by which marketers obtain genuine false reviews. To obtain the True set, Ott weeds out three categories of TripAdvisor hotel reviews for the 20 Chicago hotels simply to hold constant all non-linguistic differences between True and False reviews; these are non-5-star reviews, non-English reviews, and reviews with fewer than 150 characters. Ott uses an additional category—first-time authors—that is specifically targeted at weeding out False reviews, "since these opinions are more likely to contain opinion spam, which would reduce the integrity of our truthful review data [Wu et al., 2010]." [2] The remaining reviews are presumed to be True.

Larcker and Zakolyukina's ground truth tagging has a problem similar to Ott's: verifying false claims is straightforward, based on financial restatements, but verifying true claims is not as clear. In addition, though, the truth of financial claims is subject to change over time as restatements may flip a claim from T to F. Ott's liars also clearly know they are lying; L&Z's narrators may not know about a financial manipulation at the time of the conference call.

In their 2014 paper, Fornaciari and Poesio establish both gold and silver standards for their Amazon book reviews through reasoning about which reviews are likely to have been purchased. The silver standard is based on the presence/absence of a set of four different cues of deception.

---

[2]Wu et al. [2010] look for the "proportion of positive singletons," capitalizing on the idea that a large number of one-time reviews for a single hotel have probably been purchased and will have the testable effect of distorting the hotel's rating. "First-time author" is not the same, but functions as a shortcut for Ott's purpose.

These cues can be considered heuristics, which do not provide certain information regarding the truthfulness of the reviews, but whose presence can be regarded as hints of deceptiveness. In particular, the reviews were annotated as True if characterized by 0, 1, or 2 clues of deception, as False if 3 or 4 clues were present.

The reviewer's admission that they were paid for the review of a book puts that book on a 'suspect book' list. A review was also considered deceptive if it was one of several posted within 3 days of each other since bogus reviewers are given deadlines. Reviews written under a pseudonym were also considered deceptive. The final cue of deception came from reviews of books that the reviewer had not purchased from Amazon.

The gold standard exploits the suggestions coming from the cues described above, combining them with a priori knowledge, and consequent reasoning. The False gold standard reviews include (1) reviews by Sandra Parker, a self-professed paid review writer, who purchased only three of the 22 books she reviewed on Amazon; (2) reviews of a book whose author admitted to having bought the reviews and which showed the presence of all the deception cues; and (3) reviews of other books by the reviewers in category (2). Fornaciari and Poesio's True reviews are reasoned to be True by virtue of the fact that it would be pointless to pay someone to write a review of such a book. These books include those by classic authors as well as current, highly popular authors.

Indeed, Ott et al. [2011] come a long way toward providing gold standard True and False online hotel reviews for training and testing. However, Feng et al. [2012a] provide another set of T/F hotel reviews from TripAdvisor using fake review detection heuristics explored by Feng et al. [2012b]. Both Ott's and Feng's models perform significantly worse on this second data set.

It is a bit discouraging to compare what is needed to correctly annotate the ground truth for hotel reviews as opposed to book reviews. All hotels have certain properties in common that the bogus reviewer can refer to; books lack these shared features. Plot, character, even division into chapters are not shared by all books. These differences are reflected in the amount paid for a bogus hotel review as opposed to a book review; Ott's study paid one U.S. dollar per hotel review, while Sandra Parker was paid $10-$20 for her book reviews. And the differences result in more sophisticated techniques needed to annotate ground truth for book reviews as opposed to hotel reviews. It is likely that the expansion into other types of reviews will require different techniques again. The sleuthing of Fornaciari and Poesio at least provides a model for how to establish ground truth and rank shades of gray.

We also have to consider which data is truly "gold." In Ott's data, it is easy to tell the False data since its authors, Mechanical Turkers, were instructed to write the reviews, but the truth of the True data is not known for sure. Sites that request a review after a transaction for the product has taken place, can at least guarantee that the reviewer has actually experienced the product, but TripAdvisor does not yield transactional data. Ott et al. [2013] adds other sources of hotel reviews, including Expedia, Hotels.com, Orbitz, Priceline, which do have transactional data, although Ott et al. [2013] does not say whether the transactional data was checked. It has also added Yelp, which provides consumer alerts on bogus reviews, showing evidence like a Craigslist ad paying to write reviews.

Fitzpatrick and Bachenko add an extra step to ground truth annotation in considering the unit of analysis to be the lie rather than the liar [Fitzpatrick and Bachenko, 2012]. As noted in Chapter 4, this makes sense for longer narratives, which have a mix of lies and truthful claims. The Fitzpatrick and Bachenko data is at the other extreme in terms of ground truth annotation. In annotating ground truth for the review data, even for the more difficult book reviews, it is possible to tag several reviews as False based on a single criterion; for example, 22 reviews can be marked at once as False simply because they were written by Sandra Parker. The legal testimony tagged by Fitzpatrick and Bachenko, on the other hand, involves fact checking for every verifiable proposition using external data sources (meeting minutes, emails, etc.) to verify or repudiate individual propositions. Principles of journalistic fact checking have to be followed; the credibility of a source must be evaluated, circumstantial evidence cannot be used, nor hearsay evidence, nor statements following non-factives predicates like *believe* as in *I believed that the company's financial statements were an accurate reflection of its financial condition*. Bachenko and Fitzpatrick have not explicitly listed the direct evidence that dictates a particular true or false tag in the data, but this will be needed for a shared data set to avoid disputes as to whether a particular claim is correctly labeled.

Fornaciari and Poesio [2011, 2013] have found a more straightforward route to ground truth in the Italian court system's criminal proceedings for calumny and false testimony. These trials provide the ground truth data. Do such venues exist for other languages that could provide reliable shortcuts to obtaining ground truth?

5.6   A COMMON DATA SET

Is the language of the liar consistently different from the language of the truth teller? And is the deceptive product review in any linguistic way similar to the deceptive criminal testimony or conference call? It seems that the only way to tell is to make the various real-world data sets easily available and, at best, at a single repository that could guarantee commonalities in format, annotation, and access that would enable easy comparisons.

The amount of research and stepwise improvement that has been generated from the contribution of Ott's freely available positive and negative hotel review data is testimony to the value of a common data set. A common data set would also facilitate testing of distance measures between diverse narratives, as well as the development of a shared task in the detection of verbal deception.

5.7   CUE CLUSTERING

DePaulo et al. [2003], in considering ways in which their analyses may have underestimated the ability of cues to separate truths from lies, note that "the degree to which lies can be discriminated from truths could potentially be improved if combinations of cues were considered" [DePaulo et al., 2003, p. 104]. Similarly, Vrij [2008] argues for considering clusters of cues for both non-verbal and verbal behavior: "Looking at individual cues is searching for the verbal equivalence of Pinocchio's growing nose, which does not exist. Conversely, examining a cluster of verbal cues has yielded successful classifications in 67% to 80% of truth tellers and liars (Bond and Lee, 2005; Colwell, Hiscock, and Memon 2002; Newman, Pennebaker, Berry, and Richards, 2003; Zhou, Burgoon, Twitchell, Qin and Nunamaker, 2004b). However, different researchers examined different verbal clusters. It is unknown to what extent a certain cluster that works in one situation or one group of participants also works in another situation or with another group of participants" [Vrij, 2008, p. 108].

Bachenko et al. [2008] explicitly describe the clustering algorithm they use to improve classification, but do not consider different combinations of cues. Clearly, however, automation of cue identification enables experimentation to determine whether certain cue combinations are more successful in identifying deception, and, if so, whether different combinations are more successful in one context than another.

Similar considerations may also apply to techniques that use only n-grams as "cues." It may well be worth examining the n-grams that are most highly discriminatory in distinguishing True from False narratives. Fornaciari and Poesio [2014] take this discriminatory power into account as a "feature" in their Learning from Crowds algorithm.

5.8 CORRELATION OF VERBAL WITH NONVERBAL CUES

DePaulo et al. [2003] cite several studies that show a correlation between particular non-verbal behaviors and deception; those that showed a significant correlation across the board, including pressed lips, fewer illustrative gestures, and fidgeting, were mentioned in Chapter 2; other non-verbal behaviors show significant differences under the influence of moderators like motivation to lie, where reduction in eye contact and foot and leg movements, as well as increased nervousness and tenseness were significantly different for liars. The work of Paul Ekman and his colleagues also argues for the role of facial musculature in identifying deception, in particular [Ekman, 2001].

For the studies cited in DePaulo, the questions that present themselves to NLP are whether the physical behavior correlates with the verbal behavior and whether both can be automatically observed and synchronized. Vrij and Mann consider this issue absent the question of automation [Vrij and Mann, 2004].

The Ekman work is at one remove from this since the facial micro-expressions do not show deceit directly. Rather, they are regarded as showing emotions such as anger, fear, and disgust, which the speaker may be trying to conceal. The question here, then, is whether the emotion that is detected matches with the verbal statement or is at odds with it, in which case deception would be assumed.

Papers by Bettadapura [2009] and Sandbach et al. [2012] provide overviews of recent work in the automatic recognition of non-verbal behavior. We do not know of published research that has attempted to yoke this behavior with language.

5.9   CONCLUSION

The automatic detection of verbal deception has come a long way in a short time, from Burgoon et al. [2003] accuracy score of 60% on mock-theft laboratory data to Feng and Hirst's 91.3% accuracy on real-world hotel reviews. Much of the success has come from dealing with real-world data, limiting the topic and, therefore, the vocabulary of the data, and, recently, from sharing the data. Moving to real-world applications gives us the opportunity to test the findings from research in psychology, applied psychology, and forensics on real-world data, but it also gives us the ability to use the simplest NLP techniques to differentiate True from False language and test whether there really are differences in the way liars express themselves.

Limiting the topic enabled Ott et al. (2011) to begin to consider whether there is a relationship between deceptive language and imaginative language—a consideration supported by applied psychology research in Reality Monitoring. Topic limitation has also enabled us to begin to consider the impact of contextual factors on deception as we assemble data from related but contextually different types of reviews.

As we assemble data from related domains as well as diverse domains, we can begin to examine whether this diversity will demand quite different techniques for identifying deception that are dependent on the domain.

The storage of data tagged for ground truth also enables us to test whether the various verbal cues that have been correlated with deceptive behavior have more impact when clustered together and, if so, which clusters are more highly correlated with deception. And as bodily movements and facial gestures become more amenable to computer analysis and storage, the correlation of the physical attributes with the verbal cues will become more possible.

All of these advances are predicated on the sharing of the most expensive resource in deception studies: the sharing of data annotated for ground truth. We hope that the work we conclude here will move the discipline in that direction.

Bibliography

Adams, S. (1996). Statement analysis: What do suspects' words really reveal? *FBI Law Enforcement Bulletin*, pages 12–20. 4, 33, 36

Adams, S. (2002). *Communication under stress: indicators of veracity and deception in written narratives*. PhD thesis, Virginia Polytechnic Institute and State University. 5, 33, 75, 78

Adams, S. and Jarvis, J. (2006). Indicators of veracity and deception: an analysis of written statements made to the police. *International Journal of Speech, Language and the Law*, 13(1). 33, 37, 38, 39, 41, 46, 49, 75, 78

Agosti, A. and Rellini, A. H. (2007). The Italian LIWC dictionary. Technical report, LIWC.net. 73

Allen, J. J. B. and Mertens, R. (2009). Limitations to the detection of deception: true and false recollections are poorly distinguished using an event-related potential procedure. *Social Neuroscience*, 4(6):473–490. DOI: 10.1080/17470910802109939. 11

Almela, A., Valencia-Garcia, R., and Cantos, P. (2012). Seeing through deception: A computational approach to deceit detection in written communication. In *Proceedings of the EACL 2012 Workshop on Computational Approaches to Deception Detection*, pages 15–22. Association for Computational Linguistics. DOI: 10.5195/lesli.2013.5. 73, 80

American Polygraph Association (2010). www.polygraph.org. Accessed: April 14, 2014. 9, 10

Bachenko, J., Fitzpatrick, E., and Schonwetter, M. (2008). Verification and implementation of language-based deception indicators in civil and criminal narratives. In *Proceedings of the 22nd International Conference on Computational Linguistics - Volume 1*. CoLing, 2008. 41, 46, 49, 68, 80, 86

Beinlich, I. A., Suermondt, H. J., Chavez, R. M., and Cooper, G. F. (1989). *The ALARM Monitoring System: A Case Study with Two Probabilistic Inference Techniques for Belief Networks*. Springer. DOI: 10.1007/978-3-642-93437-7_28. 79

Bergström, Z. M., Anderson, M. C., Buda, M., Simons, J. S., and Richardson-Klavehn, A. (2013). Intentional retrieval suppression can conceal guilty knowledge in ERP memory detection tests. *Biological Psychology*, 94(1). DOI: 10.1016/j.biopsycho.2013.04.012. 11

Bettadapura, V. (2009). Face expression recognition and analysis: the state of the art. *Emotion*, pages 1–27. 87

Biber, D., Johansson, S., Leech, G., Conrad, S., Finegan, E., and Quirk, R. (1999). *Longman Grammar of Spoken and Written English*, volume 2. Pearson Education Ltd. 83

Bond, C. F. and Paulo, B. M. D. (2006). Accuracy of deception judgments. *Personality and Social Psychology Review*, 10(3):214–234. DOI: 10.1207/s15327957pspr1003_2. 54

Buller, D. B. and Burgoon, J. K. (1996). Interpersonal deception theory. *Communication Theory*, 6(3):203–242. DOI: 10.1111/j.1468-2885.1996.tb00127.x. 14, 16, 17

Buller, D. B., Burgoon, J. K., Buslig, A., and Roiger, J. (1996). Testing interpersonal deception theory: The language of interpersonal deception. *Communication Theory*, 6(3):268–289. DOI: 10.1111/j.1468-2885.1996.tb00127.x. 14, 16

Burgoon, J. K., Blair, J. P., Qin, T., and Nunamaker, J. (2003). *Intelligence and Security Informatics*, volume 2665 of *Lecture Notes in Computer Science*, chapter Deception detection through linguistic analysis, pages 91–101. Springer. 67, 81, 87

Burgoon, J. K., Enos, F., Fitzpatrick, E., Franklin, A., Newman, M., and Twitchell, D. (2004). Deception detection in written and spoken language. Technical report, Center for the Advanced Study of Language. 57, 67

Burgoon, J., Mayew, W. J., Giboney, J. S., Elkins, A. C., Moffitt, K., Dorn, B., and Spitzley, L. (2015). Which Spoken Language Markers Identify Deception in High-Stakes Settings? Evidence From Earnings Conference Calls. *Journal of Language and Social Psychology*, 0261927X15586792. 47, 51

Chen, X., Chandramouli, R., and Koduvayur, P. S. (2014). Scam detection in Twitter. In *Data Mining for Service*, number 3 in Studies in Big Data, pages 133–150. Springer. DOI: 10.1007/978-3-642-45252-9_9. 60, 66

Chu, W.-S., Torre, F. D. L., and Cohn, J. F. (2013). Selective transfer machine for personalized facial action unit detection. In *2013 IEEE Conference on Computer Vision and Pattern Recognition (CVPR)*, pages 3515–3522. DOI: 10.1109/CVPR.2013.451. 13

Clark, W. (2008). Written and oral statement analysis in the detection of deception. In *Workshop at Third International Conference on Investigative Interviewing*. Ecole Nationale de Police du Quebec, Nicolet, Quebec. 37

Cohen, J. (1988). *Statistical Power Analysis for the Behavioral Sciences*. L. Erlbaum Associates. 19

Damphousse, K. R. (2008). Voice stress analysis: Only 15 percent of lies about drug use detected in field test. *National Institute of Justice Journal*, 259:8–12. 10

Davis, M., Markus, K. A., Walters, S. B., Vorus, N., and Connors, B. (2005). Behavioral cues to deception vs. topic-incriminating potential in criminal confessions. *Law and Human Behavior*, 29(6):683–704. DOI: 10.1007/s10979-005-7370-z. 45, 46, 49

DePaulo, B. M., Lindsay, J. J., Malone, B. E., Muhlenbruck, L., Charlton, K., and Cooper, H. (2003). Cues to deception. *Psychological Bulletin*, 129(1):74–118. DOI: 10.1037/0033-2909.129.1.74. 4, 6, 12, 13, 14, 15, 17, 18, 19, 21, 22, 23, 24, 26, 27, 28, 33, 64, 69, 75, 81, 85, 86

DePaulo, Bella M. and Robert Rosenthal and Carolyn R. Green and Judith Rosenkrantz (1982). Diagnosing deceptive and mixed messages from verbal and nonverbal cues. *Journal of Experimental Social Psychology*, 18(5):433–446. DOI: 10.1016/0022-1031(82)90064-6. 75

Driscoll, L. N. (1994). A validity assessment of written statements from suspects in criminal investigations using the SCAN technique. *Police Studies*, 17(4). 37, 38, 41, 46, 48, 49

Ekman, P. (1981). Mistakes when deceiving. *Annals of the New York Academy of Sciences*, 364:269–278. DOI: 10.1111/j.1749-6632.1981.tb34479.x. 15

Ekman, P. (2001). *Telling Lies: Clues to Deceit in the Marketplace, Politics, and Marriage*. W.W. Norton. 13, 14, 15, 86

Ekman, P. (2003). Darwin, deception, and facial expression. *Annals of the New York Academy of Sciences*, 1000(1):205–221. DOI: 10.1196/annals.1280.010. 15

Ekman, P. and Friesen, W. V. (1969). Nonverbal leakage and clues to deception. *Psychiatry*, 32(1):88–106. 14

Ekman, P. and Friesen, W. V. (1974). Detecting deception from the body or face. *Journal of Personality and Social Psychology*, 29(3). DOI: 10.1037/h0036006. 12, 13

Ekman, P., Friesen, W. V., and Simons, R. C. (1985). Is the startle reaction an emotion? *Journal of Personality and Social Psychology*, 49(5):1416. DOI: 10.1037/0022-3514.49.5.1416. 14

Ekman, P. and O'Sullivan, M. (1991). Who can catch a liar? *American Psychologist*, 46:913–920. DOI: 10.1037/0003-066X.46.9.913. 54

Ekman, P. and O'Sullivan, M. (2006). From flawed self-assessment to blatant whoppers: The utility of voluntary and involuntary behavior in detecting deception. *Behavioural Sciences & the Law*, 24:673–686. DOI: 10.1002/bsl.729. 14

Ekman, P., O'Sullivan, M., and Frank, M. (1999). A few can catch a liar. *Psychological Science*, 10(3):263–266. DOI: 10.1111/1467-9280.00147. 54

Ekman, P., O'Sullivan, M., Friesen, W. V., and Scherer, K. R. (1991). Invited article: Face, voice, and body in detecting deceit. *Journal of Nonverbal Behavior*, 15(2):125–135. DOI: 10.1007/BF00998267. 14

Elkins, A. C., Derrick, D. C., and Gariup, M. (2012). The voice and eye gaze behavior of an imposter: automated interviewing and detection for rapid screening at the border. In *Proceedings of the EACL Workshop on Computational Approaches to Deception Detection*, pages 49–54. Association for Computational Linguistics. 12

Feng, S., Banerjee, R., and Choi, Y. (2012a). Syntactic Stylometry for Deception Detection. In *Proceedings of the 50th Annual Meeting of the Association for Computational Linguistics (Volume 2: Short Papers)*, pages 171–175, Jeju Island, Korea. Association for Computational Linguistics. 4, 75, 84

Feng, S., Xing, L., Gogar, A., and Choi, Y. (2012b). Distributional Footprints of Deceptive Product Reviews. In *Proceedings of the 2012 International AAAI Conference on WebBlogs and Social Media*, volume 18, pages 98–105. 76, 84

Feng, V. W. and Hirst, G. (2013). Detecting deceptive opinions with profile compatibility. In *Proceedings of the 6th International Joint Conference on Natural Language Processing, Nagoya, Japan*, pages 14–18. 5, 76

Fisher, R. P. and Geiselman, R. E. (1992). *Memory-Enhancing Techniques for Investigative Interviewing: The Cognitive Interview*. Charles C. Thomas. 32

Fitzpatrick, E. and Bachenko, J. (2010). Building a forensic corpus to test language-based indicators of deception. In *Corpus-linguistic Applications: Current Studies, New Directions*, Language and Computers: Studies in Practical Linguistics, pages 183–196. Rodopi. 44

Fitzpatrick, E. and Bachenko, J. (2012). Building a data collection for deception research. In *EACL 2012 Proceedings of the EACL Workshop on Computational Approaches to Deception Detection*, pages 31–38. Association for Computational Linguistics. 44, 45, 57, 83, 85

Fleming, J. H. (1994). Multiple-audience problems, tactical communication, and social interaction: A relational-regulation perspective. *Advances in Experimental Social Psychology*, 26:215. DOI: 10.1016/S0065-2601(08)60155-0. 23

Fornaciari, T. and Poesio, M. (2011). Lexical vs. surface features in deceptive language analysis. In *Proceedings of the 13th International Conference on Artificial Intelligence and Law*. 72, 80, 85

Fornaciari, T. and Poesio, M. (2013). Automatic deception detection in Italian court cases. *Artificial Intelligence and Law*, pages 1–38. DOI: 10.1007/s10506-013-9140-4. 25, 43, 45, 46, 48, 85

Fornaciari, T. and Poesio, M. (2014). Identifying fake Amazon reviews as learning from crowds. In *Proceedings of the 14th Conference of the European Chapter of the Association for Computational Linguistics*, pages 279–287. DOI: 10.3115/v1/E14-1030. 54, 65, 86

Gokhman, S., Hancock, J. T., Prabhu, P., Ott, M., and Cardie, C. (2012). In search of a gold standard in studies of deception. In *EACL 2012 Proceedings of the EACL Workshop on Computational Approaches to Deception Detection*. 83

Graciarena, M., Shriberg, E., Stolcke, A., Enos, F., Hirschberg, J., and Kajarekar, S. (2006). Combining prosodic lexical and cepstral systems for deceptive speech detection. In *Proceedings of the 2006 International Conference on Acoustics, Speech and Signal Processing*. IEEE. DOI: 10.1109/ICASSP.2006.1660200. 12

Haddad, D., Walter, S., Ratley, R., and Smith, M. (2001). Investigation and evaluation of Voice Stress Analysis technology. Technical report, Air Force Research Laboratory, Rome, NY. 10

Harnsberger, J. D., Hollien, H., Martin, C. A., and Hollien, K. A. (2009). Stress and deception in speech: Evaluating layered voice analysis. *Journal of Forensic Sciences*, 54(3):642–650. DOI: 10.1111/j.1556-4029.2009.01026.x. 10

Hedges, L. V. and Olkin, I. (1985). *Statistical Methods for Meta-analysis*. Academic Press. 19

Heinrich, C. U. and Borkenau, P. (1998). Deception and deception detection: The role of cross-modal inconsistency. *Journal of Personality*, 66(5):687–712. DOI: 10.1111/1467-6494.00029. 75

Hernández Fusilier, D., Montes-y-Gómez, M., Rosso, P., and Guzmán Cabrera, R. (2014). Detecting positive and negative deceptive opinions using PU-learning. *Information Processing & Management*. DOI: 10.1016/j.ipm.2014.11.001. 64, 66, 77

Hess, U. and Kleck, R. E. (1990). Differentiating emotion elicited and deliberate emotional facial expressions. *European Journal of Social Psychology*, 20:369–385. DOI: 10.1002/ejsp.2420200502. 14

Hill, M. L. and Craig, K. D. (2002). Detecting deception in pain expressions: The structure of genuine and deceptive facial displays. *Pain*, 98:135–144. DOI: 10.1016/S0304-3959(02)00037-4. 14

Hirschberg, J., Benus, S., Brenier, J. M., Enos, F., Friedman, S., Gilman, S., Girand, C., Graciarena, M., Kathol, A., and Laura Michaelis, e. a. (2005). Distinguishing deceptive from non-deceptive speech. *Proceedings of Eurospeech'05*. 75

Horvath, F. (1978). An experimental comparison of the psychological stress evaluator and the galvanic skin response in detection of deception. *Journal of Applied Psychology*, 63. DOI: 10.1037/0021-9010.63.3.338. 75

Horvath, F. (1979). Effect of different motivational instructions on detection of deception with the psychological stress evaluator and the galvanic skin response. *Journal of Applied Psychology*, 64(3). DOI: 10.1037/0021-9010.64.3.323. 75

Horvath, F. (1982). Detecting deception: the promise and the reality of voice stress analysis. *Journal of Forensic Sciences*, 27(2):340–351. 10

Horvath, F., Jayne, B., and Buckley, J. (1994). Differentiation of truthful and deceptive criminal suspects in behavior analysis interviews. *Journal of Forensic Sciences*, 39:793–807. 43

Horvath, F., McCloughan, J., Weatherman, D., and Slowik, S. (2013). The accuracy of auditors' and layered voice analysis (LVA) operators' judgments of truth and deception during police questioning. *Journal of Forensic Sciences*, 58(2):385–392. DOI: 10.1111/1556-4029.12066. 10

Humpherys, S. L., Moffitt, K., Burns, M. B., Burgoon, J. K., and Felix, W. F. (2011). Identification of fraudulent financial statements using linguistic credibility analysis. *Decision Support Systems*, 50:585–594. DOI: 10.1016/j.dss.2010.08.009. 47, 50

Inbau, F., Reid, J., Buckley, J., and Jayne, B. (2011). *Criminal Interrogation and Confessions*. Jones & Bartlett Publishers. 28

Johnson, M. and Raye, C. L. (1981). Reality monitoring. *Psychological Review*, 88:67–85. DOI: 10.1037/0033-295X.88.1.67. 35, 71

Johnson, M. K., Foley, M. A., Suengas, A. G., and Raye, C. L. (1988). Phenomenal characteristics of memories for perceived and imagined autobiographical events. *Journal of Experimental Psychology: General*, 117(4):371–376. DOI: 10.1037/0096-3445.117.4.371. 35

Kasl, S. V. and Mahl, G. F. (1965). Relationship of disturbances and hesitations in spontaneous speech to anxiety. *Journal of Personality and Social Psychology*, 1(5):425. DOI: 10.1037/h0021918. 23

Keenan, J. P., Rubio, J., Racioppi, C., Johnson, A., and Barnacz, A. (2005). The right hemisphere and the dark side of consciousness. *Cortex*, 41:695–704. DOI: 10.1016/S0010-9452(08)70286-7. 1

Keila, P. S. and Skillicorn, D. B. (2005). Detecting unusual and deceptive communication in email. In *Centers for Advanced Studies Conference*, pages 17–20. 70

Köhnken, G. (2004). Statement Validity Analysis and the 'detection of the truth'. In *The Detection of Deception in Forensic Contexts*, pages 41–63. Cambridge University Press. DOI: 10.1017/CBO9780511490071.003. 34

Köhnken, G., Schimossek, E., Aschermann, E., and Höfer, E. (1995). The cognitive interview and the assessment of the credibility of adults' statements. *Journal of Applied Psychology*, 80(6). DOI: 10.1037/0021-9010.80.6.671. 75, 78

Koper, R. J. and Sahlman, J. M. (1991). The behavioral correlates of real-world deceptive communication. In *The 41st Annual Meeting of the International Communication Association*. 43, 47, 48, 51

Lafferty, J. C., Eady, P. M., and Elmers, J. (1974). The desert survival problem. *Experimental Learning Methods*. 68

Larcker, D. F. and Zakolyukina, A. A. (2010). Detecting deceptive discussions in conference calls. Technical report, Rock Center for Corporate Governance/ Stanford University. 47, 50, 51, 72, 80

Li, D. and Santos, E. S. (2012). Argument formation in the reasoning process: toward a generic model of deception detection. In *Proceedings of the EACL Workshop on Computational Approaches to Deception Detection*, pages 63–71. Association for Computational Linguistics. 79

Lin, D. (1998). An information-theoretic definition of similarity. In *Proceedings of the 15th International Conference on Machine Learning (ICML-98)*. 83

Lippold, O. (1971). Physiological tremor. *Scientific American*, 224(3). DOI: 10.1038/scientificamerican0371-65. 10

Mann, S., Vrij, A., and Bull, R. (2002). Suspects, lies and videotape: An analysis of authentic high-stake liars. *Law and Human Behavior*, 26(3):365–376. DOI: 10.1023/A:1015332606792. 45, 49

Mann, S., Vrij, A., and Bull, R. (2004). Detecting true lies: police officers' ability to detect suspects' lies. *Journal of Applied Psychology*, 89(1):137. DOI: 10.1037/0021-9010.89.1.137. 54

Mann, W. C. and Thompson, S. A. (1988). Rhetorical structure theory: Towards a functional theory of text organization. *Text*, 8(3):243–281. 78

Marcus, M. P., Santorini, B., and Marcinkiewicz, M. A. (1993). Building a large annotated corpus of English: The Penn treebank. *Computational Linguistics*, 19(2):313–330. 53

Mehrabian, A. (1977). *Nonverbal Communication*. Aldine. 23

Meissner, C. A., Redlich, A. D., Bhatt, S., and Brandon, S. (2012). Interview and interrogation methods and their effects on true and false confessions. *Campbell Systematic Reviews*. 29

Mihalcea, R. and Strapparava, C. (2009). The Lie Detector: Explorations in the Automatic Recognition of Deceptive Language. *Proceedings of the ACL-IJCNLP Conference Short Papers*, pages 309–312. DOI: 10.3115/1667583.1667679. 54, 60, 76, 80, 81

Nahari, G., Vrij, A., and Fisher, R. P. (2012). Does the truth come out in the writing? SCAN as a lie detection tool. *Law and Human Behavior*, 36(1):68–76. DOI: 10.1037/h0093965. 37, 39, 40, 41

National Research Council (2003). *The Polygraph and Lie Detection*. Haworth Press, Washington, D.C. 9, 10

Newman, M. L., Pennebaker, J. W., Berry, D. S., and Richards, J. M. (2003). Lying words: Predicting deception from linguistic styles. *Personality and Social Psychology Bulletin*, 29(5):665–675. DOI: 10.1177/0146167203029005010. 54, 55, 70, 80

Ott, M., Choi, Y., Cardie, C., and Hancock, J. T. (2011). Finding deceptive opinion spam by any stretch of the imagination. In *Proceedings of the 49th Annual Meeting of the Association for Computational Linguistics*, pages 309–319. Association for Computational Linguistics. 36, 54, 57, 58, 61, 62, 68, 71, 76, 77, 80, 81, 82, 83, 84

Ott, M., Cardie, C., and Hancock, J. T. (2013). Negative deceptive opinion spam. In *Proceedings of the 2013 Conference of the North American Chapter of the Association for Computational Linguistics: Human Language Technologies,*, pages 497–501, Atlanta, Georgia, USA. Association for Computational Linguistics. 54, 63, 81, 84

Pavlidis, I., Eberhardt, N. I., and Levine, J. A. (2002). Seeing through the face of deception. *Nature*, 415:35. DOI: 10.1038/415035a. 11

Pennebaker, J. W., Chung, C. K., Ireland, M., Gonzales, A., and Booth, R. J. (2007). *The development and psychometric properties of LIWC2007*. LIWC.net, Austin, TX. 4, 70

Pennebaker, J. W. and Francis, M. E. (1996). Cognitive, emotional, and language processes in disclosure: Physical health and adjustment. *Cognition and Emotion*, 10:601–626. DOI: 10.1080/026999396380079. 70

Pennebaker, J. W., Mayne, T. J., and Francis, M. E. (1997). Linguistic predictors of adaptive bereavement. *Journal of Personality and Social Psychology*, 72(4):863–871. DOI: 10.1037/0022-3514.72.4.863. 70

Petrov, S. and Klein, D. (2007). Improved inference for unlexicalized parsing. In *Proceedings of the 2007 Conference of the North American Chapter of the Association for Computational Linguistics: Human Language Technologies,*, volume 7, pages 404–411. 75

Pollina, D. A., Dollins, A. B., Senter, S. M., Brown, T. E., Pavlidis, I., Levine, J. A., and Ryan, A. H. (2006). Facial skin surface temperature changes during a "concealed information" test. *Annals of Biomedical Engineering*, 34(7):1182–1189. DOI: 10.1007/s10439-006-9143-3. 11

Porter, S. and Yuille, J. C. (1996). The language of deceit: An investigation of the verbal clues to deception in the interrogation context. *Law and Human Behavior*, 20(4). DOI: 10.1007/BF01498980. 37, 39, 40, 41, 75

Quinlan, J. R. (1993). *C4.5: Programs for Machine Learning*. Morgan Kaufmann. 67

Rabon, D. (1996). *Investigative Discourse Analysis*. Carolina Academic Press. 33, 37

Ramirez-Esparza, N., Pennebaker, J., Garcia, F. A., and Raquel Suria-Martinez, e. a. (2007). La psicologia del uso de las palabras: Un programa de computadora que analiza textos en español. *Sociedad Mexicana de Psicologia*. 74

Raskin, D. C. and Esplin, P. W. (1991). Statement Validity Assessment: Interview procedures and content analysis of children's statements of sexual abuse. *Behavioral Assessment*. 33

Raykar, V. C., Yu, S., Zhao, L. H., Hermosillo Valadez, G., Florin, C., Bogoni, L., and Moy, L. (2010). Learning from crowds. *The Journal of Machine Learning Research*, 11:1297–1322. 66

Rayson, P., Wilson, A., and Leech, G. (2001). Grammatical word class variation within the British National Corpus sampler. *Language and Computers*, 36(1):295–306. 71, 82, 83

Reiter, C. (2007). Travel websites clamp down on bogus reviews. online. Accessed: October 12, 2014. 62

Resnik, P. (1995). Using information content to evaluate semantic similarity in a taxonomy. In *Proceedings of the International Joint Conference on Artificial Intelligence*. 83

Rissman, J., Greely, H. T., and Wagner, A. D. (2010). Detecting individual memories through the neural decoding of memory states and past experience. *Proceedings of the National Academy of Sciences*, 107(21):9849–9854. DOI: 10.1073/pnas.1001028107. 12

Rubin, V. L. and Vashchilko, T. (2012). Identification of truth and deception in text: Application of vector space model to Rhetorical Structure Theory. In *Proceedings of the EACL Workshop on Computational Approaches to Deception Detection*, pages 97–106. Association for Computational Linguistics. 4, 78

Rudacille, W. C. (1994). *Identifying Lies in Disguise*. Kendall/Hunt, Dubuque, IO. 33

Sandbach, G., Zafeiriou, S., Pantic, M., and Yin, L. (2012). Static and dynamic 3D facial expression recognition: A comprehensive survey. *Image and Vision Computing*, 30:683–697. DOI: 10.1016/j.imavis.2012.06.005. 87

Santos, E. J. and Li, D. (2010). On deception detection in multiagent systems. *Systems, Man and Cybernetics, Part A: Systems and Humans, IEEE Transactions on*, 40(2):224–235. DOI: 10.1109/TSMCA.2009.2034862. 78

Sapir, A. (1987). Scientific Content Analysis. Technical report, Phoenix: Laboratory for Scientific Interrogation. 33

Saxe, L., Dougherty, D., and Cross, T. (1985). The validity of polygraph testing: Scientific analysis and public controversy. *American Psychologist*, 40(3):355–366. DOI: 10.1037/0003-066X.40.3.355. 9

Shaw, D. J., Vrij, A., Leal, S., Mann, S., Hillman, J., Granhag, P. A., and Fisher, R. P. (2013). Expect the unexpected? variations in question type elicit cues to deception in joint interviewer contexts. *Applied Cognitive Psychology*, 27(3):336–343. DOI: 10.1002/acp.2911. 31, 32

Smith, N. (2001). Reading between the lines: An evaluation of the scientific content analysis technique (SCAN). Technical report, Home Office. Policing and Reducing Crime Unit, Research, Development and Statistics Directorate. 37, 39, 46, 49, 50

Sporer, S. L. (1997). The less travelled road to truth: verbal cues in deception detection in accounts of fabricated and self-experienced events. *Applied Cognitive Psychology*, 11(5):373–397. DOI: 10.1002/(SICI)1099-0720(199710)11:5%3C373::AID-ACP461%3E3.3.CO;2-S. 35, 75

Sporer, S. L. (2004). Reality monitoring and detection of deception. In Granhag, Pär Anders and Strömwall, Leif A., editor, *The Detection of Deception in Forensic Contexts*, pages 64–102. Cambridge University Press. 36, 40

Steller, M. (1989). Recent developments in statement analysis. In Yuille, J., editor, *Credibility Assessment*, pages 135–154. Kluwer, Deventer, The Netherlands. 36

Steller, M. and Köhnken, G. (1989). Criteria-based content analysis. In Raskin, D. C., editor, *Psychological Methods in Criminal Investigation and Evidence*, pages 217–245. Springer-Verlag. 33, 34, 78

Streeter, L. A., Krauss, R. M., Geller, V., Olson, C., and Apple, W. (1977). Pitch changes during attempted deception. *Journal of Personality and Social Psychology*, 35(5). DOI: 10.1037/0022-3514.35.5.345. 12

Strömwall, L. A., Bengtsson, L., Leander, L., and Granhag, P. A. (2004). Assessing children's statements: The impact of a repeated experience on CBCA and RM ratings. *Applied Cognitive Psychology*, 18(6):653–668. DOI: 10.1002/acp.1021. 36

Trankell, A. (1963). *Vittnespsykologins Arbetsmetoder*. Liber. 33

Trovillo, P. V. (1939). History of lie detection. *Journal of Criminal Law and Criminology*, 29(6):848–881. 2

Undeutsch, U. (1954). Die Entwicklung der gerichtspsychologischena Gutachtertätigkeit. [The historical development of the use of expert psychological testimony]. In Wellek, A., editor, *Bericht uber den 19, Kongress der Deutschen Gesellschaftfür Psychologie*, Gottingen. Verlag für Psychologie. 3

Undeutsch, U. (1967). Beurteilung der Glaubhaftigkeit von Aussagen [Veracity assessment of statements]. In Undeutsch, U., editor, *Handbuch der Psychologie: Vol. 11. Forensische Psychologie*, pages 26–181. Hogrefe, Gottingen, Germany. 33

Undeutsch, U. (1989). The development of statement reality analysis. In Yuille, J. C., editor, *Credibility Assessment*, pages 101–119. Springer. 33, 78

Valla, L. (2008). *On the Donation of Constantine*. The I Tatti Renaissance Library (Book 24). Harvard University Press. 3

Vrij, A. (2005). Criteria-based content analysis: A qualitative review of the first 37 studies. *Psychology, Public Policy, and Law*, 11(1):3–41. DOI: 10.1037/1076-8971.11.1.3. 35, 44

Vrij, A. (2008). *Detecting Lies and Deceit: Pitfalls and Opportunities*. Wiley Series in the Psychology of Crime, Policing and Law. John Wiley & Sons, 2nd edition. 3, 6, 9, 12, 13, 16, 32, 36, 37, 40, 41, 69, 86

Vrij, A. and Granhag, P. A. (2012). Eliciting cues to deception and truth: What matters are the questions asked. *Journal of Applied Research in Memory and Cognition*, 1(2):110–117. DOI: 10.1016/j.jarmac.2012.02.004. 28, 29

Vrij, A. and Mann, S. (2001a). Telling and detecting lies in a high-stake situation: the case of a convicted murderer. *Applied Cognitive Psychology*, 15:187–203. DOI: 10.1002/1099-0720(200103/04)15:2%3C187::AID-ACP696%3E3.0.CO;2-A. 43, 45, 49

Vrij, A. and Mann, S. (2001b). Who killed my relative? Police officers' ability to detect real-life high-stake lies. *Psychology, Crime and Law*, 7(1-4):119–132. DOI: 10.1080/10683160108401791. 54

Vrij, A. and Mann, S. (2004). Detecting deception: The benefit of looking at a combination of behavioral, auditory, and speech content related cues in a systematic manner. *Group Decision and Negotiation*, 13(1):61–79. DOI: 10.1023/B:GRUP.0000011946.74290.bc. 86

Vrij, A., Mann, S., Leal, S., and Fisher, R. (2010). 'Look into my eyes': can an instruction to maintain eye contact facilitate lie detection? *Psychology, Crime & Law*, 16(4):327–348. DOI: 10.1080/10683160902740633. 11, 30, 31

Vrij, A., Mann, S. A., Fisher, R. P., Leal, S., Milne, R., and Bull, R. (2008). Increasing cognitive load to facilitate lie detection: the benefit of recalling an event in reverse order. *Law and Human Behavior*, 32(3):253. DOI: 10.1007/s10979-007-9103-y. 29, 30

Warmelink, L., Vrij, A., Mann, S., Leal, S., Forrester, D., and Fisher, R. P. (2011). Thermal imaging as a lie detector tool at airports. *Law and Human Behavior*, 35(1):40–48. DOI: 10.1007/s10979-010-9251-3. 11

Wiener, M. and Mehrabian, A. (1968). *Language within Language: Immediacy, a Channel in Verbal Communication*. Ardent Media. 23, 78

Wu, G., Greene, D., Smyth, B., and Cunningham, P. (2010). Distortion as a validation criterion in the identification of suspicious reviews. In *Proceedings of the First Workshop on Social Media Analytics*, pages 10–13. ACM. DOI: 10.1145/1964858.1964860. 83

Zaparniuk, J., Yuille, J. C., and Taylor, S. (1995). Assessing the credibility of true and false statements. *International Journal of Law and Psychiatry*, 18(3):343–352. DOI: 10.1016/0160-2527(95)00016-B. 75

Zhou, L., Burgoon, J. K., Nunamaker, J. F., and Twitchell, D. (2004a). Automating linguistics-based cues for detecting deception in text-based asynchronous computer-mediated communications. *Group Decision and Negotiation*, 13(1):81–106. DOI: 10.1023/B:GRUP.0000011944.62889.6f. 68, 70

Zhou, L., Burgoon, J. K., Twitchell, D. P., Qin, T., and Nunamaker, J. F. (2004b). A comparison of classification methods for predicting deception in computer-mediated communication. *Journal of Management Information Systems*, 20(4):139–166. 54, 67, 68, 70, 80

Zuckerman, M., DeFrank, R. S., Hall, J. A., Larrance, D. T., and Rosenthal, R. (1979). Facial and vocal cues of deception and honesty. *Journal of Experimental Social Psychology*, 15(4):378–396. DOI: 10.1016/0022-1031(79)90045-3. 75

Zuckerman, M., Paulo, B. M. D., and Rosenthal, R. (1981). Verbal and nonverbal communication of deception. In Berkowitz, L., editor, *Advances in Experimental Social Psychology*, volume 14, pages 1–57. Academic Press, New York. 14, 15

Zuckerman, M., Driver, R., and Koestner, R. (1982). Discrepancy as a cue to actual and perceived deception. *Journal of Nonverbal Behavior*, 7(2):95–100. DOI: 10.1007/BF00986871. 14, 75

Zuckerman, M. and Driver, R. E. (1985). Telling lies: Verbal and nonverbal correlates of deception. *Multichannel Integrations of Nonverbal Behavior*, pages 129–147. 14

Authors' Biographies

JOAN BACHENKO

Joan Bachenko is president of Linguistech LLC and serves as adjunct faculty in Linguistics at Montclair State University. Previously she worked on NLP and speech technology at the Naval Research Laboratory in Washington D.C. and AT&T Bell Laboratories in Murray Hill, NJ. She left Bell Laboratories to co-found Linguistic Technologies, Inc. (LTI) in Minnesota, where she directed R&D projects on speech recognition systems for medical applications and served on the graduate faculty of the University of Minnesota. After the sale of LTI she began her current work on deception. Dr. Bachenko holds three software patents and has published papers on speech, parsing, and deceptive language.

EILEEN FITZPATRICK

Eileen Fitzpatrick is a professor in the Linguistics Department at Montclair State University. Previously she was a member of the technical staff at AT&T Bell Laboratories in Murray Hill, NJ. She has been the principal investigator on several Department of Defense contracts involving the annotation of narrative data and modeling of classifiers to predict deception. She is the author of papers on corpus building and modeling of deceptive narrative. Dr. Fitzpatrick served for six years on the Institutional Review Board at Montclair State, where she dealt with the privacy constraints on the collection of real world and laboratory data.

TOMMASO FORNACIARI

Tommaso Fornaciari is an Investigative Psychologist with the Italian National Police. Since obtaining his Ph.D. at the University of Trento, he has carried out research activities in forensic linguistics, publishing studies in which computational methods are employed with the aim of detecting deception in text and in transcripts of spoken language from criminal proceedings. He presently works at the Department of Public Security of the Italian Ministry of the Interior, engaged in research and technological innovation for public security. Prior to that, he worked at the Forensic Science Police Service, where he dealt with criminal analysis, mostly regarding violent murders.